AUTHORS DIGEST

THE WORLD'S GREAT STORIES IN BRIEF, PREPARED
BY A STAFF OF LITERARY EXPERTS, WITH
THE ASSISTANCE OF MANY
LIVING NOVELISTS

ROSSITER JOHNSON, Ph.D., LL.D.

EDITOR-IN-CHIEF

ISSUED UNDER THE AUSPICES OF THE
AUTHORS PRESS

W. BOVGVEREAV. 1883.

AUTHORS DIGEST

VOLUME XVIII

MYTHOLOGY AND FOLK-LORE

For to pass the time this book shall be pleasant to read in , but for to give faith and belief that all is true that is contained herein, ye be at your liberty.—*William Caxton.*

WITH AN ANALYTICAL INDEX

Issued under the auspices of the
AUTHORS PRESS

PREFACE

A S the mythologies or folk-lore of the various peoples are here brought together, the reader will be able to compare them readily and cannot fail to observe their striking differences —from the gloomy and despotic notes of the Oriental and the Egyptian to that which borders on the playful and hilarious in the North American. And this appears the more singular from the fact that while the former belong to ancient civilizations, the latter is the production or heritage of a people in the Stone Age.

The mythologies of Greece and Rome are so intermingled as to be largely identical—in fact, the Roman is hardly more than the Greek transplanted, but with notable change of names. Thus the Greek Athene is the Roman Minerva, the Greek Here is the Roman Juno, the Greek Aphrodite is the Roman Venus, the Greek Poseidon is the Roman Neptune, and the Greek Hermes is the Roman Mercury.

The great story of the destruction of Troy, as given in Volume X, stops where the *Iliad* stops, with the death of Hector. The subsequent wanderings of Ulysses are narrated in this volume. Also, there is an outline of the *Æneid* in Volume XVII, here supplemented with a particularized account of the settlement in Italy. The *Eddas* are presented in Volume VIII. The remaining Icelandic legends are almost devoid of interest for the general reader, but we have selected one, Gunnar's horse-fight, for a place here. The other Scandinavian countries are represented in due proportion. As for the Anglo-Saxon, all minor ones are dwarfed by the Arthurian legends; and from Sir Thomas Malory's great book we have made such selections as, taken consecutively, give the gist of the whole story.

R. J.

out of his chambers in the east in his golden chariot drawn by milk-white steeds, he receives the oblation of all true worshipers. At evening, he rolls away in a sea of splendor, but he leaves his crimson mantle on the mountain peaks, as a sign that his adorers should kneel and receive his parting blessing. He is known also as Yurya and Mitra. There are twelve Adityas, or sun-gods of the months, in addition to the supreme Aditya. They are inviolable, imperishable beings, and dwell in eternal light. They are neither sun, moon, stars, nor dawn, but the eternal sustainers of the luminous life which exists behind these appearances.

Adon-Tammuz (*Assyrian* and *Phenician*). The sun-god of Assyria and also of Phenicia. He was beloved by the goddess Baalath. This aroused the jealousy of Baal-Moloch, the Fiery, who sent a fierce boar to attack him when hunting in the forests of Lebanon. The death of the young god occurred in July, and that month was sacred to him. The river that flowed by Gebal, in which city was his finest temple, was named after him, and in his month flowed red with blood. He came to life again, however, for six months every year. His festival was celebrated in spring. It began with processions of wailing women, tearing their hair and shrieking: "Ailanu! Tammuz is dead!" Then, after all the funeral rites had been performed over the bier upon which lay his statue, a triumphant cry arose: "Adon is living!"

Adon-Tammuz is the Adonis of Greek mythology. In the Babylonian Nimrod epic he is mentioned as the beloved of Ishtar (Astarte or Ashtoreth, the Semitic goddess corresponding to Aphrodite), being represented there as slain by the goddess herself. The name is written variously as Adon-Thammuz, Tammuz, and Thammuz.

Adonai (*Hebrew*). "Lords." The name read in place of the ineffable name Yahveh (Jehovah) wherever this occurs in the Old Testament. Yahveh, the national name of the God of Israel, became more and more an object of superstitious reverence to the Jews, and when the Greek translation (the Septuagint) of the Old Testament was made, the Greek equivalent, "Kyrios" (Lord), for Adonai was used wherever the word Yahveh occurred in the original. The writers of the New Testament followed the same practise. Further, the Jews wrote under the consonants, Y H V H, which represented the word Yahveh in the Old Testament, the vowels of the word Adonai, E, O, A, as a direction that this name should be read. In ignorance of this fact the early translators of the Bible into European languages supposed that these vowels were to be inserted among the consonants above them, and so transliterated the name of the God of Israel as Yehovah. In Germanic languages J is the letter of the sound indicated in English by Y. Accordingly, in passing from German and kindred translations into English, the pronunciation of the word was further distorted into Jehovah.

Æshma Daeva (*Persian*). The demon of anger in the Zend Avesta. He is identified with Asmodeus, of the Book of Tobit in the Hebrew Apocrypha.

Agastya (*Hindu*). He was the son of Mitra and Varuna. He was born in a water-jar as "a fish of great luster"; and, being only a span in length, received the surname of Mana. He commanded the Vindhya mountains to prostrate themselves before him, and that is why they have lost their primeval altitude. He is called the Ocean-drinker; for he drank up the ocean, partly because it had offended him, partly because he wished to help the gods in their wars with the Daityas when the latter had hidden themselves in the waters. Afterward he was made ruler of the star Canopus, which bears his name. According to the Maha-bharata, his ancestors were suspended by the heels in one of the hells, and could only be rescued by his son. He formed, then, a most beautiful maiden out of the most graceful parts of the different animals—the eyes of the *fawn*, etc.—and made her his wife. He is a very prominent figure in the Ramayana. There he is the king of the hermits of the Vindhya mountains and keeps the demon Rakshasas in order. He received Rama with the greatest kindness and bestowed on him the bow of Vishnu. When Rama was restored to his kingdom, Agastya accompanied him to Ayodhya as his adviser. He holds a high place in the Indian Pantheon, and is even said to have introduced the Hindu religion into the Peninsula.

Aghasura (*Hindu*). An asura, or demon, who was the general of Kansa, King of Mathura. He was the second cousin of Krishna. He took the form of a huge serpent, and the cowherds who were the companions of Krishna, mistaking his hole for a cavern, entered it. They were rescued by Krishna.

Agni (*Hindu*). The god of fire. He is one of the triad of chief gods, which is composed of Agni, Indra, and Surya, who preside respectively over earth, air, and the sky. The Vedas represent him as the conveyor of the sacrifices of mortals to the gods, and, in general, as the messenger of men, their priest, their protector against the terror and horrors of darkness, and the defender of their homes. More hymns in the Vedas are addressed to him than to any other god. The Agni-purana is supposed to have been communicated to Agni by Vasishtha, but it is of late origin and has no legitimate claim to be regarded as a Purana. It is devoted to the glorification of Shiva.

Ahalya (*Hindu*). She was the wife of Gautama, one of the Rishis, or inspired sages. She was the first woman made by Brahma, who bestowed her on Gautama. The god Indra fell in love with her, and, assuming the form of her husband, succeeded in deceiving her. For this reason, the Rishi expelled her from his hermitage and deprived her of the prerogative of being the most beautiful woman in the world. She was restored to her natural state by Rama, and her husband became reconciled to her.

Ahura-Mazda, corrupted into Ormazd (*Persian*). He was the supreme god of Irân, the creator of the other gods, and the ruler of them all. The rivers are his brides, the sun is his eye, the lightnings are his children, and he wears the heavens as a star-spangled garment. Man, according to his deeds, belongs to Ahura or to his enemy Angra-Mainyu (Ahriman). He belongs to the former if he helps him by his own good thoughts, deeds, and works, if he sacrifices to him, and if he makes the realm of Angra-Mainyu smaller by destroying his creatures. On the other hand, if he slay the creatures of Ahura, he will be classed with demons. Animals also belong to one spirit or the other, according as they are incarnations of either the god or the fiend. The killing of animals belonging to Ahura is an abomination like killing the god himself. The Yazatas, or angels of Ahura, are numbered by thousands, and each is to be reverenced. In answer to the holy sage Zarathushtra (Zoroaster) the god revealed all that men should know. It is written down in the sacred book called the Zend Avesta.

Airavata (*Hindu*). The prototype of the elephant, produced at the making of Amrita, the water of immortality. He is Indra's beast of burden.

Aitareya (*Hindu*). A sage to whom a Brahmana, an Aranyaka, and a Upanishad were revealed. Each bears his name.

Aja (*Hindu*). A sun-god. He was the father of Dasharata, the seeming parent of Rama, who was really an incarnation of

Vishnu. On his way to a Svayamvara (tournament), he was annoyed by a wild elephant, and ordered it to be shot at once. No sooner was the animal pierced by an arrow than a most beautiful figure issued from it. It was that of a Gandharva, or celestial musician, who had been transformed into a mad elephant for mocking a Brahman. It had been foretold him that, after ages had passed, he should be liberated from his degrading condition by Aja. As soon as Dasharata had grown up, Aja gave him his arrows and ascended to the heaven of Indra.

Ajigarta (*Hindu*). A poor Brahman Rishi or sage. King Hariscschandra vowed that if he obtained a son he would sacrifice him to Varuna. Rohita was born to him, and Ajigarta sold the King his son Sunahsepa to be a substitute for the Prince.

Al Araf (*Mohammedan*). A partition between heaven and hell occupied by those who have not yet entered paradise, but hope to do so. It is regarded by some as a limbo for the patriarchs and prophets, or other holy persons, and by others as a place of abode for those whose good and evil works are about equally balanced.

Al Borak (*Mohammedan*). "Lightning." A winged animal white in color, between a mule and an ass in size, and of great swiftness, on which Mohammed is said to have made a nocturnal journey to the seventh heaven, conducted by the angel Gabriel.

Al Rakim (*Mohammedan*). A dog that accompanied and guarded the Seven Sleepers.

Al Sirat (*Mohammedan*). The bridge over hell, across which all must pass who enter paradise. It is of inconceivable narrowness, finer than the edge of a razor; hence those burdened by sins are sure to fall off, and are dashed into perdition. The same idea appears in Persian and in Hebrew mythology.

Amarushataka (*Hindu*). An erotic poem, mystically interpreted, written ostensibly by a king named Amaru, but by some attributed to the philosopher Sankara, who assumed the dead form of Amaru in order to converse with his widow.

Amesha Spentas (*Persian*). The seven supreme spirits of Avestan theology. At their head as their creator stands Ahura-mazda. The others are moral or physical abstractions; Vohu Manah, "good mind," Asha Vahishta, "best righteousness," Khshathra Vairya, "the wished-for kingdom," Spenta Armaiti, "holy harmony," Haurvatat, "saving health," and Ameretat, "immortality." In the later religion they became guardian geniuses respectively of the flocks, fire, metals, the earth, waters, and trees. They bear the same relation to Ahura-mazda as do the Adityas (*q.v.*) in Vedic theology to Varuna. Their name in modern Persian is Amshaspands.

Amrita (*Hindu*). Ambrosia, or the water of immortality. This nectar of the gods had been lost, with the result that they were conquered in battle and robbed of their strength. Vishnu gave orders to have the ocean churned into a new nectar which, he declared, would at once restore their supernatural power and enable them to destroy their enemies. The gods first gathered all plants and herbs and cast them into the waters. Then they took the mountain Mandara for a churning-stick and Vasuki, the serpent, for a rope, while Vishnu himself, in the form of a tortoise, became a resting-place for the mountain. Thereupon they churned the ocean until they had produced the ambrosial food of immortality. Seated on a lotus, Shri, the goddess of beauty, and many other lovely beings arose out of the waves. Then came forth the physician of the gods, Dhanvantari, bearing aloft the cup longed for by gods and demons. And, indeed, the demons would have carried off the precious liquid but for the intervention of Vishnu. Then, after the hosts of heaven had quaffed the draught, their strength was renewed, and they struck down their foes, who fell headlong through space to the lowest depths of hell. Afterward the Amrita was stolen by Garuda, the bird of Vishnu, but it was recovered by Indra.

Anaitis (*Syrian*). A Syrian goddess whose worship was introduced into Greek mythology. She was variously identified with Artemis, Aphrodite, Cybele, etc. In Egyptian mythology she appeared under the name Anta, or Antha.

Anakim (*Hebrew*). A race of giants dwelling in southern Palestine. They were probably pre-Canaanitish people of large stature magnified into giants by the apprehensive imagination of the immigrant Israelites, who created a legendary lore concerning them, calling them refaïm (the dead, the phantoms), and confounding them with the Titanic races overwhelmed in the deluge.

Anandalahari (*Hindu*). "The Wave of Joy." A poem ascribed to Sankara. It is a hymn of praise to Parvati, wife of Shiva. It is mingled with mystical doctrine.

Anasuya (*Hindu*). Wife of the Rishi Atri. According to the Ramayana, she lived in the forest of Dandaka, which was infested by Rakshasas and other hideous demons.   But she did not fear them because of the power given her by her austerities, which had brought rain, fruits, and flowers during a ten-years' dearth.   She even compelled the sacred Ganges to flow near her dwelling.   She received Sita, the wife of Rama, with affection, and bestowed upon her the boon of eternal youth and beauty.

Andhaka, the " Blind Walker " (*Hindu*).   The demon son of Kasyapa.   He had one thousand arms and the same number of heads, as well as two thousand eyes and feet.   He was named Andhaka because he walked as if he were blind.   He was slain by Shiva when he was trying to carry off from the paradise of Indra the Parajata tree, one of the beautiful things that came into existence at the churning of the ocean, and which formed "the delight of the nymphs of heaven."   For this feat Shiva was honored with the title of Andhakaripu, Andhaka's foe.

Angiras (*Hindu*).   He was the father of Agni, the god of fire, and was not only one of the Maharishis, or great Rishis, but was also one of the ten Prajapatis, or creators of mankind.   In later times, he became an inspired lawgiver and a writer on astronomy. As an astronomical personification, he is the Brihaspati, or regent of the planet Jupiter.   His sons, whom he had by the wife of Rathitara, a childless member of the Kshatriya, or "Kingly soldier" caste, were called Angirasas.   These Angirasas (descendants of Angiras) were endowed with Brahmanical glory, and, as their father was the father of Agni, they are regarded as the children of the fire-god. At a later period the descendants of Angiras became the personifications of luminous bodies, of celestial phenomena, and of the divisions of time.   They are also specially charged with the protection of sacrifices performed according to the rules laid down in the Atharva-veda.

Angra-Mainyu, Ahriman (*Persian*).   He is the serpent or evil principle, the source of falsehood, darkness and death.   Many sins may be atoned for by killing the creatures of the enemy of Ahura. The struggle between good and evil is limited, for the world is not to last forever, and in the end he will be vanquished by means of a sacrifice performed by Ahura and the priest-god Sraosha.

Aniruddha, "the Uncontrolled" (*Hindu*).   He was the grandson of the god Krishna, and was married to his cousin, Subhara.   A Daitya princess, named Usha, the daughter of the demon King Bana, fell in love with him, and, by means of magical enchantments, allured him to her apartments in the palace of her father's city, Sonita-pura. When Bana learned of the adventure he sent guards to seize Aniruddha. The valiant youth, however, took hold of an iron club that lay near him and slew all his assailants. Bana then made use of his magical powers, and secured him. Krishna, on discovering the plight of his grandson, came to the rescue, followed by his son and brother. A great battle was fought, in which Bana was aided by Shiva and by Skanda, the god of war. But he was defeated. His life was spared at the intercession of Shiva. Aniruddha was carried home by Krishna to Dvaraka, his sacred city, and Usha accompanied him as his wife.

Anu (*Hindu*). Son of King Yayati and Sarmishtha. Sukra, the father of another wife of Yayati, Devayani, pronounced a curse upon the king, but offered to transfer it to any one of his five sons who would consent to bear it. Anu was one of the four who refused, and his father therefore inflicted the curse upon him that his posterity should not possess dominion.

Anu (*Babylonian*). He was the supreme god of the sky and, in a special way, the god of the city of Erech. Although at first a Sumerian divinity, he appears to have been at once adopted by the Semites, who succeeded them as rulers of Babylonia. But as the Babylonian Semites could not conceive of a god without a goddess, we are told that out of Anu was formed Anat, the female counterpart of the god. Anu was for a time the god of the supreme State in Babylonia, and therefore supreme god of the whole country. But as the home of the kings was originally in the north, where Bel had his sanctuary, Anu and Bel came to be associated on equal terms, for, though the sovereign was priest and vicegerent of Anu, it was Bel who conferred on him his sovereignty. Gradually, however, Ea grew to be considered as on a level with Anu and Bel, and so, as the three deities exercised equal influence and power, they formed a divine triad. Still, as Anu continued to remain the god of the heavens, he would appear to have preserved a sort of superiority, even after the formation of the trinity.

Anunaki (*Babylonian*). The spirits of the earth. With the Igigi, spirits of heaven, they constitute the "host of heaven and earth," subordinate to the higher gods, especially to Anu, the supreme god of heaven.

Anunit (*Babylonian*). She was the goddess of one of the two Sipparas on the Euphrates, and for this reason the city under her protection was called "the Sippara of Anunit." Her origin was in the time when Babylonia was ruled by the Sumerians—the Turanians who preceded the Semites in the land. During that period she was known as Anunna or "the spirit of the earth," and was sexless. When Sippara became the seat of a Semitic empire, Anunna, "the spirit," was transformed into Anunit, "the goddess." For a time it looked as if Anunit, instead of Istar, would become the supreme goddess of Semitic cult. But when the dominance of Sippara passed away, she sank into the ordinary herd of Babylonian goddesses.

Apaosha, the drought-fiend (*Persian*). There is a continuous conflict during the dog-days between Apaosha and Tishtrya, the storm-god. The storm-god first attacks the fiend in the shape of a beautiful youth, then as a bull with golden horns, and at last as a white horse with golden caparison and golden ears. The drought-fiend assumes the form of a black horse, and "they meet together, hoof against hoof; they fight for three days and three nights, and then the black deeva proves too strong for bright and glorious Tishtrya. He overcomes him." Then Tishtrya flies from the sea and cries out to Ahura-Mazda that the reason of his defeat is because men do not worship him with sacrifice and praise, invoking him by his own name. If they did so, he would have the strength of ten camels, ten horses, ten bulls, ten mountains, and ten rivers. Ahura offers him a sacrifice in his own name, and the strength he wished for returns to him. Tishtrya again engages in battle with Apaosha, who flies before him. The white horse being victorious, copious rains descend, and the nymphs of the brooks rush from the hillsides, with pearly, sandaled feet, and laden with love and mercy for the sun-parched plains. Then all, nymphs and human beings, offer sacrifices to Tishtrya, and chant hymns in his praise.

Apava (*Hindu*). Apava performed the office of the creator Brahma, and divided himself into two parts, male and female. These produced Vishnu, who created Viraj, who brought into the world the first man.

Apsaras (*Hindu*). They are the nymphs of Indra's heaven. When the ocean was churned into the immortal nectar, the want of which had impaired the strength of the gods, the Apsaras sprang forth from the foam. Beautiful though they were, neither gods nor demons would consent to marry them individually, and so they became the wives of the whole host of heaven promiscuously. Their amours on earth were innumerable: they fascinated heroes and allured even austere sages from their devotions and penances. They were among the rewards granted in Indra's paradise to heroes who fall in battle. They can change their form at pleasure, are fond of games of chance, especially dice, and give luck to those able to placate them. They produce love-madness, from which, however, those who know the proper charms and incantations can protect themselves.

Arda Viraf Namak (*Persian*). "The Book of Arda Viraf." In the reign of Shapur II, doubts still existed as to the truth of the Zoroastrian religion, and the Dasturs resolved to send one among them to the land of the dead to bring back certainty. Seven were chosen, and these chose three, and these again one. He was Arda Viraf. Viraf drank three cups of a narcotic and slept until the seventh day, during which period he made a journey through heaven and hell, guided by Sraosha, "the angel of obedience," and Ataro Yazad, "the angel of fire." His book is a record of the rewards of the one place and the punishments of the other.

Arjuna (*Hindu*). The third of the five Pandava princes. Although nominally the son of the Rajah Pandu, he was really the child of the god Indra, for which reason he is sometimes called Aindra. He is the bravest, most handsome, generous, high-minded, and, in all respects, the most interesting of the Pandavas. He was taught the use of arms by Drona, and was his favorite pupil. It was his skill in all martial exercises that won Draupadi at her Svayamvara—a tournament at which the prize was always a beautiful princess (see the Ramayana). For an involuntary transgression, his sensitive conscience imposed on him a twelve-years' exile from his family. During that period he met the Naga serpent princess Ulupi, and had a son by her named Iravat. He had other wives, among them a sister of the god Krishna. After obtaining from Agni the bow Gandava, he fought by his side against his own father, Indra, and helped the fire-god to burn the Khandava forest. When his eldest brother, Yudi-shtira, lost his raj at dice, and when the five brothers decided to go on a pilgrimage with their common wife, Draupadi, he resolved to retire to the Himalayas, in order to propitiate the gods and persuade them to grant the Pandavas their peculiar weapons, for he knew that a conflict with the Kauravas was impending. He met Shiva, who was disguised as a mountaineer, and fought with him. Luckily, he recognized the god, and fell down and worshiped him. Thereupon, not only Shiva, but Indra, Varuna and the other gods bestowed upon him their weapons. Indra, after carrying him to heaven and teaching him several feats of arms, sent him against the Daityas of the sea, whom he vanquished. For his mighty deeds in the terrible struggle with the Kauravas, see the Maha-bharata. Having arranged for an Ashva-medha (horse-sacrifice) after the victory, he followed the victim with an army through many countries and cities, subduing rajahs or receiving their submission. In one city he fought unknowingly with his son, and was killed by him, but was restored to life by a Naga charm, supplied by his wife, Ulupi. After the performance of the great sacrifice, he retired from the world to a hermitage in the Himalayas.

Ariel (*Hebrew*). "Lion of God." In cabalistic angelology, he is one of the seven princes of spirits who preside over the waters, under Michael, the arch-prince.

Asanga (*Hindu*). The authorship of a great many of the hymns in the Rig-veda is attributed to him. But notwithstanding his piety he incurred the anger of the gods for some unknown reason. They cursed him, and, as a punishment, changed him into a woman. Upon his repentance he was, owing to the intercession of the Rishi Medhatithi, to whom he gave abundant wealth, restored to his male form. Most of his hymns are addressed to this Rishi.

Asari (*Babylonian*). He was the sun-god of Eridu, the ancient seaport of Babylonia on the Persian Gulf. He was the son of Ea, the chief god of the city, of whose will he was the interpreter. He communicated to men such lessons in culture and the art of healing as Ea desired them to learn. His name signifies "he who does good to man," and he was ever on the watch to assist his worshipers and to instruct them in the magic words that banish sickness and evil. Throughout Babylonia he was the champion of light and order, who conquered the demons of darkness and the dragon of chaos and anarchy. Although he died and was buried in his temple in Babylon, he rose in greater splendor than ever the next morning, and is therefore the god of the resurrection.

Ashta-vakra (*Hindu*). He was a Brahman and the son of Kahoda, whose history occupies an important place in the Maha-bharata.

a Maharsi or great saint, and also one of the ten lords of creation engendered by Manu, for the purpose of creating the human race. He was married to Anasuya, a daughter of Daksha, and therefore a granddaughter of Brahma. See the Ramayana for the details of his reception of Rama in his hermitage.

Aurva (*Hindu*). A sage, the son of Urva, and the grandson of Bhrigu. In a persecution of his race, which did not spare even the unborn child, he was miraculously preserved and brought to birth. The fire of his wrath threatened to destroy the world, when, at the intercession of the manes of his ancestors, he sent this fire into the ocean, where it has since remained.

Avalokiteshvara (*Hindu*). "The Lord Who Looks down from on High." The personification of power, the merciful protector of the world and of men. He is one of the two Bodhisattvas, the other being Manjushri, who had become objects of worship about 400 A.D. Avalokiteshvara is also known as Vajradhara, "the bearer of the thunderbolt," formerly an epithet of Indra.

Avesta (*Persian*). The Bible of Zoroastrianism. It is erroneously known as the Zend-avesta, the word Zend meaning commentary merely. It is as if we should call a Bible and Commentary, "Commentary Bible." The word Avesta means "knowledge."

Azazel (*Mohammedan*). One of the djinns who for their transgressions were taken prisoners by the angels. Azazel grew up amongst them and became their chief, until he refused to prostrate himself before Adam, when he became Iblis ("despair"), the father of the Shaitans ("evil spirits").

Azhi Dahaka (*Persian*). Originally the cloud-serpent of Aryan mythology, and the destroying serpent of the Avesta, it was later in Persia identified with an old king of Iran.

Azrael (*Hebrew* and *Mohammedan*). The angel who separates the soul from the body at the moment of death, for which he watches.

Baal (*Canaanite*). The supreme god, answering to Bel of the Babylonians. He is a personification of the male generative power, as Ashtoreth is of the female. His statue was placed on a bull, the symbol of generative power, and he was represented with pomegranates and clusters of grapes in his hands. He was also worshiped as the sun-god, and was represented with a crown of rays. Bulls and human beings, especially children, were offered to him in sacrifice [Jeremiah xix, 5]. His altars were set up on heights and the roofs of houses [Jeremiah xxxii, 29]. The cult of Baal and Ashtoreth was attended by wild and licentious orgies. Baal appears under various designations in the Old Testament as the Baal or "Lord" of places, e.g., Baal-Peor, Lord of Mount Peor, and in the New Testament he appears as Beelzebub, the Lord of Flies, or of Carrion and Corruption, of which flies are the sign. Baal was known among the Ammonites as Moloch; among the Moabites as Chemosh; among the Tyrians as Melcarth—"King of the City"; and in the confederacy of Shechem as Baal Berith—"Lord of the Covenant." The name of Baal enters into a number of Carthaginian names, such as Hannibal ("Baal is gracious"), and Hasdrubal ("Baal is helpful"). Jezebel, or Phenician princess, the daughter of Ethbaal, of Sidon, introduced the worship of Baal into Israel upon her marriage with Ahab, king of that country.

Bala-rama (*Hindu*). He was the elder brother of Krishna, and therefore, if not an incarnation, at least a son of Vishnu. Vishnu took two hairs, one black and the other white, and these became Bala and Krishna, their mother being Devaki. Bala was born fair, while Krishna was black. Bala took part in all the freaks of his brother when young, but he afterward turned out a more respectable deity. Among his earliest exploits was the killing of the demon Dhenuka, who had the form of a monstrous ass. Another demon in revenge tried to carry him off on his shoulder, but the boy beat in his temples with his fists. He was a bold and loyal supporter of Krishna in all the latter's adventures. Once he summoned the river Yamuna to come to him that he might bathe. When it disobeyed his commands, he plunged his plowshare into it and dragged the waters after him. The river was compelled to assume a human form and to ask his forgiveness. Bala differed from most of the other gods in having only one wife. He was too fond of wine, and so irascible that he sometimes quarreled even with Krishna.

Bali (*Hindu*). A Daitya who had attained sovereignty over the three worlds, but lost it when he promised Vishnu, in his dwarf incarnation, as much land as he could measure with three strides. Vishnu met the condition, and banished Bali to the under world, where he reigned over the spirits there.

Bana (*Hindu*). A Daitya with a thousand arms. He was a friend to Siva, and an enemy of Vishnu. His daughter Usha loved the grandson of Krishna, Aniruddha, and had him brought to her by magic. Krishna came to his grandson's rescue, cutting off Bana's arms in the attack. Upon Shiva's intercession Bana was spared.

Bau (*Babylonian*). She was originally a Sumerian goddess, and, although domesticated at Eridu in early days, this city was not her first home, which was probably in the north. She was the mother of the god Ea, and was known as "the great mother" from whom mankind had received their herds and flocks as well as the crops of the fields. She it was who gave fertility to the soil and protected those who tilled it. The heifer was her symbol, and during the Sumerian domination in Babylon she was probably the local spirit of some field near Eridu, appearing in the form of a heifer. But in the days when she is known to us by contemporaneous inscriptions, she is already a goddess, and has become the divine protector of the Semitic rulers of the land. And when she assumed the authority of a Semitic goddess, she became the first creatress mother, and then the mother of the creator. In the kingdom of Lagas the festival of the new year was sacred to her.

Bel (*Babylonian*). The second god in the first triad of the twelve great divinities, the members of the triad being Anu, Bel, and Ea, the gods respectively of the sky, the earth, and the sea. He is of Semitic origin, being akin to Baal (*q.v.*), although he has no solar attributes such as the Canaanite god possesses. To him was ascribed the creation of the world, and especially of men, whence the Assyrian kings called themselves "governors of Bel," and "rulers over Bel's subjects." His name means "Lord"; Belit, the feminine of the word, is represented as his consort. Bel was often entitled "the father of the gods," and Belit "the mother of the gods." It was Bel that brought about the deluge which destroyed mankind. The principal seat of his worship was Nippur. While the tutelar deity of the city of Babylon was Merodach (Marduk), this god was frequently called Bel-Merodach, and so identified by foreigners with Bel. Both Isaiah (xlvi, 1) and Jeremiah (l, 2) do this. By a similar error, Bel being known as the supreme god of Babylonia, Herodotus considered the great Nebo temple of Borsippa as that of Bel.

Bhagavatgita (*Hindu*). "The Song of Bhagavat." Bhagavat means "the adorable one," and is a name of Krishna when he is identified with the Supreme Being. The author is unknown. He is supposed to have lived in India in the first or second century of the Christian era. The poem was added to the Maha-bharata. Its philosophy is eclectic, combining elements of the Sankhya, Yoga, and Vedanta systems with the later theory of Bhakti, or "faith."

Bhairava [masc.] and **Bharavi** [fem.] (*Hindu*). The names of Shiva and his wife Devi. In the plural, Bhairavas, the word denotes the eight terrible manifestations of Shiva.

Bharata (*Hindu*). Son of Dasharatha by Kaikeyi, and half-brother of Ramachandra. Although Kaikeyi succeeding in driving Rama into exile, Bharata refused to supplant him, and went after him to bring him back and place him on the throne. On Rama's refusal to return until the end of his exile, Bharata consented to rule in his name.

Bhima (*Hindu*). A reputed son of Pandu, but in reality the son of his wife Pritha or Kunti by Vayu, the god of the wind. He was of prodigious size and strength, and had a voracious appetite.

Bhrigu (*Hindu*). A Vedic sage. He was a Prajapati, or one of the progenitors of mankind, and as such founded a branch of the human race. He was present at the sacrifice of Daksha, the son of Brahma, and, in consequence of the quarrel that ensued among the gods, had all the hairs of his beard plucked out by Shiva. He rescued the sage Agastya from the tyranny of King Agus, who had obtained supernatural power. Him Bhrigu cursed and turned into a serpent. There was once a dispute among the Brahmans during a sacrifice as to which deity was best entitled to homage at the hands of a Brahman. Bhrigu was selected as an ambassador to go to heaven and test the character of the various gods. He asked first to pay his visit to Shiva; but was told that the god was too busy to see him. Wherefore he decided that such a deity was too degraded to be fit to receive sacrifices and offerings from pious and respectable persons. He next visited Brahma, who was so inflated with his own importance that he treated the sage with scant courtesy. So Bhrigu concluded that he was unworthy the homage of Brahmans. Vishnu was asleep when he called. The sage, now thoroughly angry, was indignant at this slothfulness, and stamped with his left foot upon the breast of the god. The latter was so far from being offended that he pressed the foot, declaring that he was honored and made happy by its contact. Delighted with such humility, Bhrigu proclaimed Vishnu the only deity fit to be worshiped by gods and men.

Bodhisaltva (*Hindu*). One who has perfect knowledge as to his essence, being on his way to attain the state of a supreme Buddha.

Brahma (*Hindu*). He is the most difficult deity in the Hindu mythology to account for intelligently. As Brahma, or Brahman in the neuter gender, the name signifies passive, unconscious being. From unconsciousness and non-reality this being passed into consciousness and reality. It receives no worship, but is the object of abstract meditation, which Hindu sages practise in order to obtain absorption into it. As Brahma, of the masculine gender, he is the first member of the Hindu Triad; and is the supreme spirit manifested as the active creator of the universe. When he first created the world it remained unaltered for one of his days, and a day of Brahma is 2,160,000,000 years. Then it was consumed by fire; but the gods, the sages, and the elements survived. Brahma himself sank back into unconsciousness. As soon as he awoke, he again restored creation. This process of destruction and restoration will be repeated until his existence of a hundred years is brought to a close, a period which it requires fifteen figures to express. When this period is ended he will expire, and all the gods, sages, and the whole universe will be resolved into their constituent elements. The mode in which he created was by dividing himself into all things that exist, even the smallest stones and plants. Then, to establish the divine order of caste, he created the Brahman from his mouth, the Kshatrya, or "kingly soldier," from his arms, the husbandman, or Vaishya, from his thighs, and the Shudra, or servile caste, from his feet.

Brahmanas (*Hindu*). Writings in the Veda which relate to the brahman, or worship. They contain the oldest rituals and traditional narratives of India.

Brihaspati (*Hindu*). A deity in whom the action of the worshiper on the gods is personified. He is the supreme sacrificing priest who intercedes with the gods in behalf of men and protects them against the wicked. As the prototype of the sacerdotal order, and as family priest of the gods themselves, he is called the father of gods and men, and extended creative power is attributed to him. His epithets are: "the shining one," "the gold-colored," "he who has the thunder for his voice." He was afterward made the regent of the planet Jupiter and preceptor of the gods, and, as such, is represented as drawn by eight pale horses. When his wife Tara was carried off by the moon-god Soma, there was a terrible war among the gods, and the earth, "shaken to her very center," appealed to

Brahma to stop it. He did so by compelling Soma to restore Tara to her husband.

Buddha (*Hindu*). The name signifies "the wise," or rather "the one who understands," from *budh*, to understand. There are two different accounts of the Buddha. The Brahmans say that over every Kalpa, or new creation of the universe, which occurs at the end of a fixed period comprising more than two billion years, the creative power is assigned to one of five Buddhas. Four of these have already appeared. The last was Gautama, who lived about six hundred years before the Christian era ; but he was far inferior to his predecessor, who lived a thousand years before this epoch. He was an incarnation of Vishnu, who took flesh in the womb of Maya (Illusion) with the object of preaching a false doctrine to the Daityas, who by their works of piety and by their sacrifices were attaining a power that threatened the supremacy of the gods. The Daityas accepted the false tenets of the Buddha and became so weak that they ceased to be a danger to the gods. But the Buddhist scriptures tell a different story. The great reformer was of the solar race and was the son of Muni, King of Benares. As he belonged to the Çakya tribe, he was known as Çakya-Muni. At the age of twenty-nine he abandoned his family and meditated in solitude on the best means of saving mankind. In six years he appeared again in the world and declared himself the Buddha. He was omniscient, but his omniscience was the result of study, not of supernatural revelation, to which he did not make any pretense whatever. Still, he was in the possession of a science eternally true. He taught the ineffable happiness of an eternal and unconscious repose (Nirvana), which can only be acquired by study, meditation, renunciation of the world, and self-denial. What made him especially obnoxious to the Brahmans was his doctrine of universal equality, from the religious standpoint. He was soon surrounded by crowds of mendicants, who were enjoined to practise chastity and lead a wandering life in fraternal community with one another. He traveled for forty-five years with a constantly increasing train of followers, numbering, toward the end of his life, more than ten thousand, for whom his wealthy adherents afterward built monasteries. Çakya-Muni, who is a personage half historical, half mythological, died, according to the Ceylon scriptures, 543 B.C. European scholars, however, place his death in 478 B.C. At first his disciples did not regard him as a supernatural being. But after a time Çakya-Muni, who had always been the enemy of the gods and of sacrifices and prayers, became a god to whom sacrifices, prayers, and adoration were offered. Gradually the Buddhists fell into the worst extravagances, adopted a sort of pantheistic polytheism, and devoted themselves to sorcery, exorcism, and every sort of mystical practise. The Buddha is perpetually incarnated in the successive Dalai Lamas of Tibet.

Budha (*Hindu*). The son of Soma, and the god of the planet Mercury. When he was born, he seemed so marvelously beautiful that both Soma and Brihaspati claimed his paternity. For a long time Tara, his mother, refused to tell which of them was really his father. At last, in obedience to the command of Brahma, she declared that he was the son of Soma. Brahma gave him the name of Budha, "the wise." He has no connection, however, with Buddha, the reformer. He is the author of one of the hymns in the Rig-veda.

Chamunda (*Hindu*). He is an emanation from the goddess Durga, the wife of Shiva. She brought him forth from her forehead, in order that he might encounter and subdue the demons Chanda and Munda, who had become a terror even to the gods. He is represented as black of aspect and form, armed with a scimitar, noose, and ponderous mace, decorated with a garland of corpses, robed in the hide of an elephant, hideous with yawning mouth, lolling tongue, and bloodshot eyes, and filling the whole universe with his shouts. When he had killed the demons he bore their heads to Durga, who honored him with the names of Chanda and Munda, contracted into Chamunda.

Chanda (*Hindu*). A name of the Goddess Durga, or Devi (*q.v.*), applied to her incarnation for the purpose of destroying the demon Mahisha. This exploit is described in the Markandeya-Purana. It is celebrated in Bengal at the Durga-Puja, the festival which is held annually in honor of the goddess in October.

Chemosh (*Moabite*). He was the sun-god of the Moabites. He was for a time adored in Judah, his worship having been introduced by Solomon, and lasting until it was destroyed by one of his successors. In *Judges* he is stated to have been also the supreme god of the Ammonites, but later researches render this very doubtful, especially as their national deity is known to have been Ammon-Milcom. The discovery of the Moabite stone (now in the Louvre), in 1868, and the translation of the long inscription in which King Mesha expresses his gratitude for the aid he received from Chemosh in conquering Israel are significant as to the deity's supremacy in his kingdom. He tells us how his people had been made subject to Israel because Chemosh was angry with them. Thanks, however, to Chemosh, "who turned with favor to Mesha, he regained the cities which Israel had captured." Therefore he built a high place to Chemosh, as, indeed, Solomon had done before him. Throughout the whole inscription Mesha speaks of Chemosh as if no other god was recognized in his country. The stone itself, he says, was erected as "a stone of salvation"; for "Chemosh had mercy, and said to Mesha: 'Go, take Nebo.'" And Mesha, in obedience to the divine command, shook off the yoke of Israel, and "killed all the warriors at Ataroth." He also took from Nebo the vessels of Yahveh (Jehovah) and offered them before Chemosh. Finally, "Chemosh drove out Israel from Jahaz," and then said to Mesha: "Go down, make war against Horonaim," which belonged to Edom. Mesha sacrificed his eldest son as a thank-offering to the deity. According to St. Jerome, Chemosh was the god of generation. But Mesha speaks of him exactly as the Israelites were in the habit of speaking of Yahveh.

Dabbat (*Mohammedan*). A monster who shall arise in the last day and shall cry unto the people of the earth, that mankind have not believed in the revelations of God.

Dadhyancha, later **Dadhicha** (*Hindu*). A famous Vedic Rishi who is frequently spoken of in the sacred books. Indra taught him certain sciences, but threatened to cut off his head if he taught them to others. The Ashvins begged him to communicate his knowledge to them. He refused for a long time, but at length consented. In order to preserve him from the wrath of Indra, they struck off his head, and substituted a horse's. After the angry deity had beheaded him, the Ashvins restored the human head, which they had carefully preserved alive. As long as Dadhyancha lived on earth, the Asuras, or demons, were controlled and tranquillized by his mere look. When he ascended to heaven, however, they overspread the earth and caused fearful calamities. Indra asked him whether there were any relics of him remaining on the earth. He answered that the horse's head was still there, and could be found in a certain lake. Thereupon the god went in search of the head, "and with its bones he foiled the nine times ninety stratagems of the Asuras." Dadhyancha was instrumental in bringing about the destruction of Daksha's sacrifice.

Dagon (*Canaanite*). The national god of the Philistines. The name is usually derived from the Hebrew *dag*, meaning fish, and Dagon was probably depicted as half man and half fish, his female counterpart being Derceto, who was worshiped especially in Askalon (see Atargatis). But in Phenician *dagan* means corn, whence the Greeks supposed that Dagon was a god of agriculture. Now in Babylon there was a god Oannes, who was half man, half fish, and also was a patron of civilization. Probably Dagon and he were identical gods.

Daityas (*Hindu*). A race of giants and demons. They were the descendants of Diti, and were almost constantly at war with the gods, interfering with their sacrifices and annoying them in a variety of ways. They and the Divanas are generally associated and scarcely distinguishable from each other. In many respects they resemble the Titans of Greek mythology, but differ from them in this: they were the victors as often as they were the vanquished.

Daksha (*Hindu*). He is the son of Brahma and the chief of the Prapajatis. In the Rig-veda he is also the father and son of Aditi. He sprang from the right thumb of Brahma, and his wife sprang from the left thumb. He had sixty daughters, who became the mothers of gods, demons, men, birds, serpents, and of all living things. He gave twenty-seven of them in marriage to the moon-god, Soma, and they became the twenty-seven lunar mansions. Daksha is also father and son of the moon. An important event, frequently mentioned in the sacred books, was the sacrifice of Daksha. It was performed in honor of Vishnu, and all the gods were invited, except Shiva, because the gods had conspired to deprive him of sacrificial offerings. When Shiva discovered that he had been insulted, he was enraged and, shouting loudly, pierced the victim with an arrow. He also created a hundred thousand demigods, who rushed upon the assembled deities. "Then the mountains tottered, the earth shook, the winds roared, and the depths of the sea were overturned." The sacrifice was broken up, Indra was knocked down, Yama's own staff was broken upon him, the moon-god was pommeled, the firegod's hands were cut off, even Brahma was pelted with stones, and gods and demigods were run through or struck with arrows. Daksha himself lost his head during the conflict. At length, Vishnu seized

Shiva by the throat, compelled him to desist, acknowledge Vishnu himself as superior, and restore such of the gods as had been slain, to life. Shiva did so; but the head of Daksha could not be found, and was replaced by that of a ram.

Dasharata (*Hindu*). A son of Aja. By his wife Kaushalya he had Rama, by Kaikeyi, Bharata, and by Sumitra, Lakshmana and Shatrughna. Rama partook of half the nature of Vishnu, Bharata of a quarter, and the other two shared the remaining fourth.

Deva (*Hindu*). A god. There were thirty-three Devas—twelve Adityas, eight Vasus, eleven Rudras, and two Asvins.

Devi, the goddess, also **Maha-devi,** the great goddess (*Hindu*). She was the wife of Shiva and the daughter of Himavat, "the Himalaya mountains." Her name occurs very often in the Maha-bharata; but it is in the Puranas that she begins to assume the leading position she takes in the Hindu Pantheon. As the Sakta, or female energy of Shiva, she is invested with two natures, one mild, the other fierce. She is especially propitiated under the latter aspect, as an object of terror. She has different names according to her different forms, attributes, and actions. In her milder form she is Uma, "light," and a type of beauty; also Gauri, "the brilliant one"; the Parvati mountaineer, and Haimavati from her parentage. In her terrible form she is Durga, "the inaccessible one"; Kali, "the black"; Chandi, "the savage"; Bhairavi, "the frightful." It is in her latter character that bloody sacrifices are offered to her, and her favor propitiated by barbarous and indecent orgies. She has ten hands, and most of the hands carry weapons. As Durga she presents the appearance of a beautiful yellow woman riding on a tiger in a fierce and menacing attitude. As Kali she is represented with a black skin. She has a hideous and fearful countenance, dripping with blood, encircled by snakes, and hung around with skulls and human heads. As Vindhya-vasini, "dweller in the Vindhyas," she has a magnificent temple near Muzapur, at a spot where the Vindhya mountains approach the Ganges; there the blood before her image is never allowed to get dry. As Maha-maya, she is the great illusion.

Dhammapada (*Hindu*). "Steps of the Law." A collection of short treatises. It was translated by Max Müller.

Dhanvantari (*Hindu*). He is the physician of the gods, and was brought into existence at the churning of the ocean. He is the originator and teacher of all medical science, and in one of his births he was exempt from human infirmities. In all his births he was master of universal knowledge. He is also called, in allusion to his office at the time of the churning, Sudha-pani, "the one who carries the nectar in his hands," and Amrita, or "the immortal one." A skilful physician was spoken of as "a Dhanvantari."

Dharmashastra (*Hindu*). The whole body of the law, given in three parts: Achara, rules of conduct; Vyavahara, judicature; and Prayashchitla, penance.

Dhatri (*Hindu*). Although he is one of the Parajati, or creators, as a divinity he would seem to have no precise functions. He is a god of generation, a promoter of matrimony, and presides over domestic life. He also cures diseases and heals broken bones, etc. He is said, after they had been destroyed, to have re-created the sun, moon, sky, air, and heavens "as they were before." He is also one of the Aditi. In later mythology he is the son of Brahma, and is sometimes identical with him.

Dhritarashtra (*Hindu*). The eldest son of Vichitravirya, or Vyasa, and brother of Pandu. He had by Gandhari one hundred sons, of whom the eldest was Duryodhana. Dhritarashtra was blind, and Pandu was affected with leprosy. Both renouncing the throne, it was fought for by the sons of each, the Kauravas (so named from an ancestor of Dhritarashtra) and the Pandaves (named their father Pandu). This is the great war about which the narrative of the Maha-bharata is woven.

Dhyani Buddha (*Hindu*). A special Buddha is assigned to each of the successive worlds of existence. They are the four Buddhas ending with Gautama, and the future Buddha, Maitreya. The material Buddha is only the emanation of a Dhyani Buddha, living in the ethereal realm of mystic trance, as indicated by the word dhyani, which means trance.

Dilipa (*Hindu*). He was descended from the sun-god. On one occasion he failed to pay due respect to Surabhi, "the cow of fortune." The divine animal at once cursed him, and predicted that he should never have offspring until he and his wife had carefully tended her daughter Vandini. They were obedient, and nursed the calf with the greatest diligence. On one occasion Dilipa risked his own life to save her from the jaws of the lion of Shiva. In due time the curse was removed, and a son, named Raghu, was born to Dilipa.

Diti (*Hindu*). She was the daughter of Daksha, the wife of the self-born Kashyapa, and the mother of the Daityas. She asked her husband to give her a son of such irresistible strength that he would be able to destroy the god Indra. He said to her: "If with thoughts holy and pious you carefully carry the babe in your womb for a hundred years, I will do so." But Indra became aware of his danger. He visited Diti in disguise, offered his services, waited on her with the utmost humility, and watched for his opportunity. It came, on the very last day of the hundred years, when Diti retired to rest without washing her feet, thereby committing a sin. Indra by means of his thunderbolt divided the unborn child into seven portions, and each of the seven portions into seven additional portions. The infant was deeply grieved at such a cruel mutilation, and wept loudly and bitterly. As Indra was unable to pacify it, he lost his temper, and again divided each portion into seven portions. In this fashion were formed the bright, swift-moving Maruts, or storm-gods. They are called Maruts from the words "Ma-rodih, do not weep," which Indra had used to still their cries.

Dodo (*Moabite*). The name of a deity found on the Moabite stone (see Chemosh) who is supposed to have been worshiped with Yahveh by the ten tribes of Israel.

Draupadi (*Hindu*). She was the daughter of King Draupada, and the wife of the five Pandu princes. She was the most beautiful woman in the world, and all the rajahs of India came to the Svayam-vara, or tournament, at which she was to be the prize of the bravest and best of them. Arjuna, the third of the Pandu brothers, won her by his skill in archery. He told his mother that he had won a prize, without specifying what it was. She answered that he must divide it with his brothers. As to disobey the orders of a mother in such circumstances was to incur the wrath of the gods, this answer created dismay, and the five brothers laid the case before the sage Vyasa. He declared that Draupadi was the incarnation of a maiden lady who had offered five sacrifices to Shiva in order to obtain a husband. Shiva informed her that she could not have a husband in this life, but that in the next she should have one for each of her sacrifices. In vain the lady assured the god that she did not want five husbands in her next life, she only wanted one in her present life. The divine decrees were irrevocable, and so Draupadi had to marry the five Pandu brothers. Draupadi is the heroine of the Maha-bharata, and her adventures were innumerable. She was the first to fall dead during the painful pilgrimage of the Pandu brothers to the heaven of Indra, but her husbands found her there when they arrived.

Drona (*Hindu*). The teacher of military art to the Kaurava and Pandava princes. In the great war of the Maha-bharata he sided with the Kauravas, and after the death of Bhishma became their leader. On the fifteenth day of the great battle he was killed by Dhrishtadyumna.

Drupada (*Hindu*). Father of Draupadi. He was beheaded on the fourteenth day of the great battle of the Maha-bharata by Drona.

Duhshasana (*Hindu*). One of the hundred sons of Dhritarashtra. When the Pandavas lost their wife Draupadi in gambling with Duryodhana, Duhshasana dragged her away by the hair of her head, and otherwise ill-used her. For this Bhima vowed he would drink his blood, a vow which he performed on the sixteenth day of the great battle.

Dur-Vasas, "the Ill-clad" (*Hindu*). He was a son or rather an emanation of Shiva, was noted for his irascible temper, and many fell under his curse. He cursed Sakuntala for not having opened her door with sufficient speed when he knocked, and was thus the cause of alienating the love of King Dushyanta from her for a time. He blessed Kunti, however, and promised that she would have a son by the sun-god. He cursed Indra because the god had treated contemptuously a garland which he had presented to him. The curse took the shape of a prediction that "his sovereignty over the three worlds would be subverted." Because of this curse Indra and the other gods grew so weak that they were easily overpowered by the Asuras, until the ocean was churned and the amrita, or water of life, produced. It is said in the Maha-bharata that on one occasion the sage was hospitably entertained by Krishna, who unluckily forgot to wipe the fragments of food from his feet. Thereupon Dur-Vasas became wild with anger, and foretold the death of the god.

Duryodhana (*Hindu*). "Hard to Conquer." Eldest son of Dhritarashtra, and the leader of the Kaurava princes in the great war of the Maha-bharata. On the death of Pandu, father of the Pandavas Dritarashtra, their uncle, brought them into his court, and had them educated with his sons. Jealousies arose between the cousins, Duryodhana taking a special dislike to the Pandava Bhimi from his skill in the use of the club. He poisoned Bhima, who was, however, restored to life by the Nagas. Duryodhana caused the Pandavas to be exiled. On his return he gambled with Yudhishthira, and won from him Draupadi, the wife in common of the Pandavas, all their possessions, and even their freedom. In the great battle that finally resulted he fell by the club of Bhima, who had vowed to break his thigh.

Dushyanta (*Hindu*). He was a descendant of the lunar deity and the husband of Sakuntala. Her separation from him and her restoration to his favor through the discovery of his token-ring in the belly of a fish form the plot of the Sakuntala by Kali-dasa, one of the great dramas of the world.

Dyaus, the heavens, or the god of the heavens (*Hindu*). In the Vedas Dyaus is a male deity, and is usually called Dyaus-pitri, the father of the heavens; cf. Zeus, Ju-piter, Dyava-Prithivi signify the heavens and the earth, and are represented as the universal parents of gods as well as of men. In some of the Vedic hymns, however, they are spoken of as created, and there are many deep speculations as to their respective origin and priority. In one hymn it is asked: "Which of these two was the first? Which the last? How were they produced? Who knows?" Most of the sacred books favor the opinion that the earth was the first of created things.

Ea (*Babylonian*). The third of the first triad of the twelve great gods. He was the god of the ocean and the waters underneath the earth. He was also lord of counsel, a protector of the people and a patron of the arts and sciences. He and his wife Dumkina are identified with Oaos and Dauke of Damascus. Their son was Merodach (Marduk).

Ea-bani (*Babylonian*). One of the heroes of the Nimrod epic. He is a bull-man, living in the desert. Coming to the city of Erech to gratify his sensual desires, he forms an alliance with Isdubar (Nimrod), and they slay Khumbaba, the usurper. (See also Izdubar.)

Ekamra (*Hindu*). A forest in Orissa which was especially beloved by the god Shiva and became the principal seat of his worship. Some of the splendid temples that were consecrated to him in this sacred spot still remain in a good state of preservation.

Gabriel (*Hebrew* and *Mohammedan*). "God is My Strong One." An archangel. In the Koran he is the revelator to Mohammed.

Gandarewa (*Persian*). A giant demon slain by Keresaspa (cf. Gandharva).

Gandhari (*Hindu*). Wife of Dhritarashtra. She loved her husband so that, because he was blind, she always wore a bandage over her eyes to be like him.

Gandharva (*Hindu*). In the Rig-veda, a celestial musician, who dwells in the air, and whose duty it is to guard the Soma. Indra obtains it for man by conquering him. Because Soma is the best medicine, Gandharva is called also the physician of the gods. He regulates the course of the horses of the sun, and he makes known the secrets of heaven. He is the parent of the first human pair, Yama and Yami. He has a peculiar influence over women, whence he is invoked in marriage ceremonies. Later, a class of Gandharvas was imagined, having the characteristics of the original.

Ganesa (*Hindu*). He was a son of Shiva and is lord of the Ganas, or bands of inferior deities, especially of those who are in immediate attendance on his father. He is also the god of wisdom and the remover of obstacles. For this reason, he is invariably propitiated at the beginning of any new enterprise, and authors invoke his aid when they begin to write. He was an author himself, and is said to have dictated the Maha-bharata to Vyasa. He is a short, fat man, of yellow color, and with a very protuberant belly; but he has the head of an elephant, with only a single tusk. One hand holds a shell, another a discus, the third a club, and the fourth a water-lily. He is sometimes represented as riding upon a rat, or with a rat attending him. His temples are very numerous, particularly in Southern India, and the number of legends that have clustered about him is past counting.

Ganga, the Ganges (*Hindu*). Ganga is both a goddess and the most sacred of rivers. When the sixty thousand sons of Sagara, King of Ayodhya, were reduced to ashes by the sage Kapila, whom they had offended, Bhagiratha, the great-grandson of Sagara, attempted to perform their funeral rites. He found he could not do so, except the goddess Ganga consented to water the ashes with her holy stream. But at this time the stream flowed through the fields of heaven. After performing the severest penances to induce the gods to send down the celestial river, he was informed that his request should be granted, but he must first secure the intervention of Shiva. Otherwise, the shock of her descent would destroy the earth, especially as the goddess was likely to be wrathful at being obliged to change her abode. At last Shiva was propitiated and consented to stand beneath the descending torrent and break its fall. He caught the river on his head, and checked its course with his matted locks. It came down in seven streams and fell into Vindu lake, whence proceed the seven sacred rivers of India. This was the most wondrous sight that had ever been witnessed. The gods rushed from every sphere in their golden chariots to behold the spectacle, and the entire universe was astonished. But the noise of the descent disturbed the sage Jahnu at a sacrifice he was performing, and in his anger he drank up the waters. He was, however, persuaded to relent by the gods, and he allowed the stream to flow out again through his ears. As a goddess, Ganga is the eldest daughter of Himavat and Mena. She is also the mother of gold by Agni, the god of fire.

Garuda (*Hindu*). The king of birds and the fearless enemy of the serpent tribe. He had the wings, talons, and beak of an eagle, but the body and limbs of a man, and was the steed upon which Vishnu usually rode along the sky. His parents were Kashyapa and Vinata, the daughter of Daksha. He inherited his hatred of serpents from his mother, who was cruelly oppressed by Kadru, the chief wife of Kashyapa and the mother of the serpents. He appeared surrounded with such a brilliant luster after his birth that the gods mistook him for Agni, the god of fire, and worshiped him. His face is white, his body golden, and his wings are red. According to the Maha-bharata, his parents gave him the power to devour wicked men, provided that he did not touch a Brahman, however bad he might be. Once, however, he swallowed a Brahman and his wife; but the Brahman burned his throat so severely that he was glad to disgorge them both. Garuda stole the amrita, or water of life, from the gods, hoping, by means of it, to purchase the freedom of his mother from Kadru. The theft was discovered by Indra, and a fierce battle ensued between the two. But although Indra was worsted, and his thunderbolt smashed, Garuda had to restore the amrita.

Gayatri (*Hindu*). The most sacred verse in the Rig-veda, as "it was milked from the Vedas." It is the duty of every Brahman to repeat it mentally in his morning and evening devotions. This prayer is addressed to the sun as Savitri, "the generator." When Gayatri or Savitri is personified as a goddess, she is regarded as the wife of Brahma, the mother of the Four Vedas, and of the twice-born or superior castes. The prayer, however, would seem to be considered by the uneducated Hindus as a simple invocation of the sun, beseeching him to shed a benign influence upon the customary offices of worship. But others attach to the text the meaning of a mystic propitiation of the spirit and essence of existence, or Brahma. The text is believed to be so holy that copyists are often afraid to transcribe it.

Gehenna (*Hebrew*). First, the valley of Hinnom near Jerusalem. From the fact that in the time of Ahaz and Manasseh children were here offered to Moloch, it became accursed when this worship had passed away, and the valley was called "Tophet" (abomination), and became a symbol of the place of punishment after death—the sense in which the word is used in the Talmud and the New Testament.

Hanuman (*Hindu*). He was the lord of the monkeys and son of Pavana, "the wind." He had the power of flying from earth to heaven and is one of the most conspicuous characters in the Ramayana for his marvelous deeds. All the monkeys under him who assisted Rama in the war against Ravana were also of superhuman origin and invested with supernatural powers. Hanuman, during the conflict, jumped from India to Ceylon in one leap, tore up trees, carried away the Himalayas, seized the clouds, and did other things equally surprising. His form was "vast as a mountain and tall as a gigantic tower; his complexion was yellow and glowing, like molten gold; he leaps into the air, and flies among the clouds, while the ocean waves are roaring and splashing below him." In one of his fights with Ravana and the Rakshasa demons, they greased his tail and set it on fire; but is was to their own great damage, for with his burning appendix he set their capital city, Lanka, in flames. His services to Rama were invaluable. When most of the hero's soldiers were incapacitated by their wounds, Hanuman flew to the Himalayas and brought thence medicinal herbs, with which he restored their strength. He killed the monster Kala-nemi and also thousands of Gandharvas, who had attacked him. The exploits of Hanuman are favorite subjects of conversation among the Hindus from childhood to old age, and paintings of scenes from his life are very common. He is worshiped by them as Yoga-chara, because of his magical powers and his skill in the arts of healing. Among his other accomplishments, his excellence as a grammarian and exegetist holds a high place. "No one excels him in learning and in ascertaining the true meaning of the scriptures. In all sciences he rivals the preceptor of the gods."

Harishchandra (*Hindu*). A king noted for his piety and justice. He purchased Shunahshephas to be offered up in place of his own son.

Harivansha (*Hindu*). A poem treating of the creation, patriarchal and regal dynasties, the adventures of Krishna, and the future of the world.

Hinayana (*Hindu*). The southern school of Buddhism.

Hiranyagarbha (*Hindu*). The one lord of all beings, who arose in the beginning of time, upholds the universe, and gives life and breath, and whom the gods obey. According to Manu he was Brahma, the first male, formed by the undiscernible First Cause in a golden egg glorious as the sun. Brahma divided the egg into two parts, which became the heavens and the earth, and placed between them the sky, the eight regions, and the eternal abode of waters.

Iddhi (*Hindu*). Power over matter possessed by the Buddhist in the fourth stage of moral perfection. In this he has gained the Abhinnas, which are "transcendent faculties"—the inner eye and ear, knowledge of all thoughts, a recollection of previous existences, and Iddhi. This last faculty enables him at will to reduce his body to the dimensions and weight of an atom, or to increase it in size and weight to any extent; to subject the elements, and to reach any object, however distant; to exercise the will to any extent, and to hold himself and others in absolute control.

Indra (*Hindu*). The god of the firmament. In the Vedas he is one of the supreme gods, but not uncreate. "A vigorous father begot him, and a heroic female brought him forth." He rides furiously through the heavens in a golden chariot drawn by "tawny steeds." In his right hand he carries the thunderbolt. He constantly recruits his strength by drinking large draughts of the intoxicating soma juice, which his devotees offer him. As the deity of the atmosphere, he governs the weather and dispenses rain. He is continually at war with Vitra, the demon of drought and inclement weather, who is overcome by his thunderbolt and forced to send down the rain to the parched earth. He is frequently represented as destroying the "stone-built cities" of the Asuras, or atmospheric demons, and of the Dasyus, or aborigines of India, who were the enemies of gods and men. In these conflicts he is sometimes escorted by the Maruts (storm-gods) and attended by his comrade Vishnu. More hymns

Kaliya (*Hindu*). A five-headed, fire-breathing serpent king. Krishna as a child jumped into his pool. Being seized by the serpent, he put his foot on the middle head and reduced him to submission, compelling him to depart to the ocean.

Kaliyuga (*Hindu*). The last and worst of the four yugas, or ages. It began February 18, 3102 B.C., and will last 432,000 years, at the end of which the world will be destroyed.

Kalki (*Hindu*). The name of Vishnu in his future character as the destroyer of the wicked and liberator of the world. It will be the tenth avatar of the god, and will take place at the end of the Kaliyuga.

Kahnashapada (*Hindu*). A king of the solar race. When hunting he encountered Shaktri, Vasishtha's eldest son and struck him with his whip. Vasishtha cursed him, so that he became a cannibal, but after twelve years restored him to his normal state.

Kalpa (*Hindu*). A day of Brahma, consisting of 1,000 yugas, or 432,000,000 years. Thirty kalpas constitute a month of Brahma, 12 months his year, and 100 years his life. The present age is the fifty-first of his years.

Kalpasutras (*Hindu*). The most sacred book of the Jainas, a Hindu sect. They devote to it five of the eight days devoted in the middle of the rainy season to reading their scriptures. It is a history of various saints, and a manual of ritual.

Kama (*Hindu*). "Wish." The god of love. In the Rig-veda, desire is the first movement that arose in the One after it had come into life through the power of abstraction. It is thus the bond between entity and nonentity. Kama is the son of Darma (justice) by Shradda (faith). Another account makes him spring from Brahma's heart. He is armed with a bow of sugar-cane and five arrows, each tipped with a different flower that symbolizes one of the five senses. He rides on a parrot or sparrow, and is attended by nymphs, one of whom bears his standard, the Makara, a fish on a red ground. His wife is Rati ("Pleasure") or Priti ("Affection"), his daughter Trisha ("Thirst" or, "Desire"), and his son Aniruddha (the "Unrestrained").

Kamahhenu (*Hindu*). A wonder-cow that gratifies all wishes.

Kansa (*Hindu*). A king who was the second cousin of Krishna. It being foretold that a son of Devaki, Krishna's mother, would destroy him, he tried to kill all her children. Bala-rama, the seventh child, was smuggled safely away, and when Krishna, the eighth, was born, his parents fled with him, whereupon the King ordered a general massacre of male infants. Kansa remained the persecutor of Krishna, but was finally killed by him.

Kanva (*Hindu*). The sage who brought up Sakuntala as his daughter.

Karna (*Hindu*). Son of Pritha or Kunti, by Surya, the son, before her marriage to Pandu, and so the unknown half-brother of the Pandava princes. He was born equipped with arms and armor. The sage Dur-Vasas had given Pritha a charm by which she might have offspring by any god she invoked, and she chose the sun. To escape disgrace she exposed the child; Adhiratha, a charioteer, found the babe, and he and Padha, his wife, reared him as their son. In the great war of the Maha-bharata Karna took the part of the Kauravas, and was killed by Arjuna. His relationship to them becoming known, the Pandavas showed his family great kindness.

Kartavirya (*Hindu*). A prince who, by worshiping the Dattatreya, a part of the divine being in which Vishnu was incarnate, obtained a thousand arms, a golden chariot answering to his will, the power of restraining wrong and enforcing righteousness, invincibility, the conquest of the earth, and finally death by a man of great renown. Finally, abusing the hospitality of the sage Jamadagni by carrying away a calf of the "cow of the sacred obligation," he was killed by Parashurama, after a struggle in which all his thousand arms were cut off.

Karttikeya (*Hindu*). "Son of the Krittakas," or Pleiades. The god of war, and the planet Mars; also called Skanda. He was the son of Shiva or Rudra, and was born without a mother, being fostered by the Pleiades. He was brought into being to destroy Taraka, a Daitya whose holiness made him formidable to the gods. He is represented as riding on a peacock, and holding a bow in one hand and an arrow in the other.

Kashyapa (*Hindu*). One of the seven sages; he is supposed to personify the race in Kashmir, which is said to be a contraction of Kashyapamira.

Kaumodaki (*Hindu*). The club of Krishna, given to him by Varuna in the fight against Indra.

Kavasha (*Hindu*). A son of a slave, who, when sacrificing on the river Sarasvati, was driven away by the Rishis as too ignoble to

PART II

EGYPTIAN MYTHOLOGY

Aah. The moon-god of Egypt. He is represented sometimes with the head of a hawk, sometimes as a child under whose shoulder hangs a tress of hair. The head is often surmounted by a disk and crescent. Occasionally we find him with the head of an ibis, adorned either with a disk and crescent or with an ostrich plume. There is a picture of him in the seventeenth chapter of the Cadet papyrus in which he sits in the middle of a boat, with a bearded human face, surrounded by four dog-headed baboons, who are evidently adoring him. His worship was so widely spread that, as a consequence, the number of his images discovered, in silver, bronze, etc., is almost innumerable. He is also the god of rebirth, rejuvenescence, and renovation.

Amon. The chief god of Thebes and eventually of all Egypt. Although incarnated in the ram, the sacred animal of Karnak, he was usually of human form, with two lofty feathers rising above his crown. It was under the Theban dynasties that he became the supreme god, first of Egypt, then of the Egyptian empire. All the other gods had to give way before him, and to lose their individuality in his. His supremacy, which began with the rise of the Eleventh and Twelfth Dynasties, was for a time checked by the Hyksos' conquest of the land. When these Asiatic barbarians were expelled, principally by the valor of the Theban princes—servants of Amon—and by the aid which he gave them, their helper in the war of independence had their exclusive devotion. Amon afterward gained their victories for them in Syria and Ethiopia. The glory and wealth of Egypt were all due to him, and therefore it was right that the spoils of Asia should be lavished on his temple and city, and that trains of captives should work for him under the lash. Amon became the one and supreme god, not by destroying, but by absorbing all the other gods. This process of fusion was aided by his identification with Ra, the sun-god, for as the Pharaoh was the son of Ra, and as Amon was the father of the Pharaoh, it logically followed that Amon and Ra were one. Thus this obscure provincial deity united with the sun-god and absorbed the rest of the gods into himself, with the result that a narrow form of polytheism passed into a materialistic pantheism, and stopped there: it never advanced into a monotheism in which the creator is separate from his creation.

Angt. A goddess personifying the lower hemisphere. She is analogous to the Greek Hestia (Roman Vesta). She was also known as Anukis.

Anubis. He was the god of embalmment, and was adored under the form of a jackal or of a human being with a jackal's head. According to the Osirian legend, he was the son of Osiris and Nepthys, the sister of Osiris. When Osiris was slain, Anubis was sent down from heaven by the sun-god Ra to assist Isis in piecing together the broken body of the murdered god. He swathed it in linen bandages, and observed all the other rites which the Egyptians were wont to perform over the bodies of the departed. When the soul was conducted into the Lower World to be judged by Osiris and the judges of the dead, Anubis, as "the director of the weight," brought forth a pair of scales, and, placing in one scale a figure or emblem of Truth, he set in the other a vase containing the good actions of the deceased. According to the side on which the balance inclined the fate of the soul was determined. During the Greek period in Egypt Anubis was identified with Hermes and took the name of Hermanubis. The Egyptian name of the god was Anpu.

Apepi. The great serpent, the embodiment of evil.

Apis. The sacred bull, or Apis, was an incarnation of Ptah (the tutelary deity of Memphis); "the new life of Ptah," he is styled on the votive tablets. The bull selected was required to be black, with a white triangle on his forehead, an eagle on his back, double hairs in his tail, and a beetle on his tongue. In this way the incarnation of the god was separated from other animals of the same species, upon whom, however, some part of his divinity was reflected. Since any bull might have become the habitation of the deity, it was necessary to treat the whole species with respect. No bull, therefore, could be slain; even at the present day, the tribes of the Upper Nile abstain from eating the ox. Although, in the eyes of the cultivated classes, the sacred bull was but a symbol of divinity, not only the Apis but the whole species was divine for the common people. A proof of this is the fact that other bulls as well as the Apis were mummified, down to a late period. With the growth of the cult of Osiris, the dead Apis became one with the god who is the lord of the other world. His identity with Ptah vanished before his newer identity with Osiris. As the Osiris bull-god, he became at first the guardian of the necropolis of Memphis, then the god of Memphis and Egypt, in life as well as in death. Gradually, under the Ptolemies, he felt the influence of Greek culture, and in the features of the human Serapis, with his majestic face and flowing beard, it was hard to recognize the bull-god of primitive Egypt.

Aten. The sun's disk. His worship was introduced by Amenhotep IV, whose other name was Khu-n-Aten, meaning "the splendor of the sun's disk." He was the tenth king of the eighteenth dynasty, and an innovator, moving the capital of Egypt from Thebes to a place in middle Egypt, the modern Tel-el-Amarna, and substituting the new worship of Aten for that of Amon and the other Egyptian deities. The change in religion was due to his marriage with a Hittite princess, who refused to worship Amon of Thebes, and clung to the sun worship of her race. The Hittite monuments bear witness to the prevalence of the worship of the sun's disk in northern Syria and even beyond. The winged solar disk appears above the figure of a king found at Birejik on the Euphrates, and at Boghaz Keni, in northern Asia Minor, it is seen carved on the rocks by ancient Hittite sculptors.

Atm, or **Atmu,** or **Tmu.** The setting sun, a double of Ra, represented in human form. It was worshiped at Northern On, or Heliopolis.

Bast. A goddess of Lower Egypt. She holds a sistrum in one hand, an ægis in the other, and has generally a basket on her arm. Although she is usually represented with the head of a cat, she has sometimes a human face, surmounted by a curly wig.

Bess. He is a hideous-looking deity, with his eyes in the top of his head, lolling tongue, and deformed legs stretched as far apart as possible. He is clad in a leopard's skin, and a plume of feathers waves above his head. As a god of war, he has a buckler and is represented brandishing a sword or drawing a bow. His statue was placed by the pillow of his worshipers, because he protected them from the evil influences of wicked spirits. He was also the god of dancing and music, and there are several pictures of him in which he plays the harp, strikes the cymbals, or dances. The Book of the Dead identifies him with Set.

Book of the Dead. The chief monument of the religious literature of Egypt, says Sayce in his "Ancient Empires," is the "Book of the Dead." Portions of it were inscribed on the mummy-cases and tombs, and are met with in the latest of the demotic papyri. It was, in fact, the funeral ritual of the Egyptians, describing in mystical language the adventures of the soul after death, and the texts it must quote in order to escape the torments and trials of the lower world. It is the literary reflection of the Osiris myth and grew along with the latter. The essence of the work dates from the Old Empire. The rest consists of additions and glosses, and glosses upon glosses, which continued to be made up to the time of the Persians. The oldest portions seem to have been of a practical moral character, contrasting strikingly with the mystical tone of the later accretions, where the doctrine of justification by faith in Osiris has taken the place of that of good works.

Busiris. A mythical king of Egypt who, to stop a famine, sacrificed to the gods every year a stranger who chanced to come within his dominions. One year, however, a sturdy foreign traveler broke the bonds with which he had been bound, and, seizing a club he carried with him, slew Busiris. It was a man of some reputation in his native country of Greece, and in foreign parts where he had traveled extensively, known as Hercules. Busiris is identified for poetic purposes by Milton with the Pharaoh who was drowned in the Red Sea.

Buto. She was the goddess of the northern half of the world, or rather of Lower Egypt. Another goddess, Nekheb, the Eileithrya of the Greeks, was the goddess of the South. Both are called the serpent goddesses, and are occasionally represented as winged serpents. They are often figured as wearing crowns: Buto, the red crown of the North; Nekheb, the white crown of the South. Buto is also represented as an Egyptian lady in the usual long dress, and with the crown of the North on her head. But, like Horus, the son of Isis, she appears most frequently with the head of a lioness. A beautiful bronze statue of the goddess, now in Copenhagen, was discovered in 1892, the lioness head of which is adorned with a round solar disk. The inscription on it says: "Give life and health to Hata, who is the friend of the goddess Buto," etc.

Hapi, " the Hidden." The hieroglyphic name of the god of the Nile. He was an inscrutable god whose abode and origin were both unknown. But he was the giver of all good things, and especially of the fruits of the earth. He was often represented as the father of the gods. He has usually a human form, with a crown of aquatic plants on his head, and holds in his hands flowers, fruits, or plants.

Hathor. She was the great Nature Mother and the Mother of Life, and was the women's especial favorite, "Lady of the Heavens" and "Queen of Beauty and of Love," as she is seen on numberless temples, walls, columns, friezes, etc. She is the heavenly cow who produced the universe and all it contained, even the sun. With her bountiful breasts she nourishes the living, and to the dead she offers bread and water on their departure from this life. Her emblem in this relation is the sycamore, which grows vigorous and bushy on the borders of the desert, and so she is often called "the Lady of the Sycamore." She was also the sovereign mistress of all the countries that border on the Red Sea from Suez to Somali. She was ultimately confounded with Isis and entered into the myth of Osiris; and she, too, had a son named Horus. She has often the human form, still oftener the head of a cow. In both cases, she holds the Tau, or key of life, has the sun-disk between her horns, and bears the lotus scepter, which was the emblem of pleasure and feasting. The Greeks identified her with Aphrodite. One of the most magnificent structures in Egypt is the temple of Hathor at Dendera. It was founded and first built by Cheops (Kufu), the Pyramid King; but has been restored, rebuilt, enlarged, through successive centuries, almost down to the beginning of the Christian era.

Horus, Horos. The Latin and Greek transcriptions of Har (the Exalted), the hieroglyphic name of the deity. He was the son of Osiris and Isis. He was always in a special manner the hawk-god and is generally, though not always, represented by the bird or with its head. In course of time, he played different parts and had different attributes entirely distinct from one another, with the result that his person was subdivided into various divinities. He united with Amon of Thebes, and became Haramon. As Harhuditi, he became the Horus of Hudit, the modern Edfu, and was preëminently the solar Horus to whom the solar disk was consecrated. As defender of his father, and son of Isis, he was Harendotes, the Greek transcript for Harnezotfi. As the hawk who was always victorious over his enemies, he was Harnubu, an epithet also given to the Pharaohs. As Horus the elder, he was conceived as representing the heavens, and formed a triad at Ombos with the earth-god and the crocodile-god. As Harpocrates, the Greek transcription of Harpakrudu, he is a child; this is denoted by the plaited lock of hair (worn by all young princes) on one side of his head and by the sucking of his finger. He wears the Pshent, or crowns of Upper and Lower Egypt, to indicate that he is worshiped in every part of the land. The Greeks, mistaking the gesture with the finger, made of him Harpocrates, the god of Silence. Sometimes he wears as a head-dress the disk and uræus or asp. As Harsomtous, the Greek transcription of Harsamtui, he is the Horus who united the two Egypts, and who, as successor of his father, Osiris, reigned over the whole country; and, as Hartomes (Greek for Hartamai), he was the Horus who pierced with his lance the serpent Apophis, and destroyed the evil powers of the night. Under the name of Harsiesis, or Horus, the son of Isis, his cult took the lead of all the others in the Delta.

Isis. The Greek transcription of the name of the goddess whom the Egyptians called, at different periods, Sait, Isait, Isit, Isi. At first her worship did not extend beyond the Delta. The original home of her cult was at Buto. There, while still a virgin, she conceived Horus by virtue of her own energy. After his birth she married her brother Osiris, and the mother, son, and putative father constituted the most celebrated triad of the Egyptian religion. She was passionately attached to Osiris, and followed him in all his transformations. When he became king of Egypt, she also ascended the throne of the living and aided him in civilizing mankind. She created medicine, united men and women in lawful union, taught them how to bruise corn between two flat stones and prepare bread. She was also the first to weave and bleach linen. When Osiris set out to conquer and civilize the world, she exercised the regency over Egypt during his absence. After the death of her husband (see Osiris) she aided her son Horus in avenging his father, and gave him material assistance in his victorious struggle with Set. Then she rejoined Osiris in his kingdom. At first Isis was represented as a woman, either alone or nursing the infant Horus. She wears all the sun tokens: the disk, the uræus (asp), and the hawk head-dress. But she is often given the cow's head, like Hathor, so that it is not always easy to know one goddess from the other. Her cult was in early times

Serapis. The Greek and Roman name of a deity of Egyptian origin, whose worship was officially promoted by the Ptolemies in order to establish a common religious bond between the Egyptians and the Greeks. Apis, who had already merged into Osiris with the growth of this latter cult, was now made to personify the Greek Hades, the world of departed spirits. A temple called the Serapeum was erected to him in Alexandria, which, says Milman in his "History of Christianity," was next to that of Jupiter in the Capitol [of Rome], the proudest monument of Pagan religious architecture. It comprehended within its precincts a vast mass of buildings, of which the temple itself formed the center. It was built on an artificial hill, in the old quarter of the city, called Rhacotis, to which the ascent was by a hundred steps. All the substructure was vaulted over; and in these dark chambers, which communicated with one another, were supposed to be carried on the most fearful and, to the Christian, abominable mysteries. All around the spacious level platform were the habitations of the priests, and of the ascetics dedicated to the worship of the god. Within these outworks of this city rather than temple was a square, surrounded on all sides with a magnificent portico. In the center arose the temple, on pillars of enormous magnitude and beautiful proportion. The work either of Alexander himself or of the first Ptolemy aspired to unite the colossal grandeur of Egyptian with the fine harmony of Grecian art. Within the temple stood the colossal statue of Serapis. This filled the sanctuary; its outstretched and all-embracing arms touched the walls; the right the one, the left the other. It was said to have been the work of Sesostris; it was made of all the metals fused together—gold, silver, copper, iron, lead, and tin; it was inlaid with all kinds of precious stones; the whole was polished and appeared of an ivory color. The measure or bushel, the emblem of productiveness or plenty, crowned its head. By its side stood the symbolic three-headed animal, one the forepart of a lion, one of a dog, one of a wolf. In this the Greeks saw the type of their poetic Cerberus. The serpent, the symbol of eternity, wound round the whole, and returned resting its head on the hand of the god. The Serapeum, says Milman, appeared secure in the superstition which connected this inviolable sanctuary, and the honor of its god, with the rise and fall of the Nile, with the fertility and the existence of Egypt, and, as Egypt was the granary of the East, the existence of Constantinople. It was, however, doomed by the growth of Christianity. Theodosius the Great, who was under ecclesiastical subjection to Bishop Ambrose, caused it to be destroyed.

Set. Another hieroglyphic name for him was Tubhon, which the Greeks transcribed as Typhon. He was originally a god of the earth and particularly of the desert. He does not seem to have been regarded as a wicked deity until he was involved in the myth of Osiris and Isis, his brother and sister. Then he personified the principle of evil, darkness, sterility. Filled with hatred of the benevolent god, he plotted against him during his absence from Egypt and killed him on his return. Horus, the son of Isis, attacked and conquered him. According to some accounts, he also put him to death; but this is doubted, because evil always survives. Set, who had rendered himself odious to gods and men, became a monster, sometimes with the head of a crocodile, sometimes with that of a hippopotamus, and sometimes with a hundred heads, all ugly and red-haired. Originally red-haired men were sacrificed to him, but, with the progress of civilization, red oxen were substituted. The ass, crocodile, hippopotamus, scorpion, and boar are sacred to him.

Sphinx, The. A colossal statue at Gizeh, Egypt, near the Great Pyramid, than which, say the archeologists, it is older. It consists of the crouching body of a lion and a human head and breast, hewn from the natural rock, with the cavities filled in with masonry. The body is 140 feet long, the head extends 30 feet from forehead to chin, and is 14 feet wide. The eyes and nose have been mutilated by Mohammedan fanatics. A low, broad head-dress extends on either side. Between the paws were found an altar, a crouching lion, with fragments of others, and three large inscribed tablets enclosing the whole, forming a sort of shrine. The Sphinx is thought to be a local personification of the sun, probably an image of Horus. Maspero, in his "Egyptian Archeology," speaking of the antiquity of the statue, says that perhaps we should not be far wrong if we ventured to ascribe it to the generations before Mena, called in the priestly chronicles "the Servants of Horus." Hewn in the living rock, at the extreme verge of the Libyan plateau, it seems, as the representative of Horus, to uprear its head in order to be the first to catch sight of his father, Ra, the rising sun, across the valley. For centuries the sands have buried it to the chin, yet without protecting it from ruin. Its battered body preserves but the general form of a lion's body. The paws and breast, restored by the Ptolemies and the Cæsars, retain but a part of the stone facing with which they were then clothed in order to mask the ravages of time. The lower part of the head-dress has fallen, and the diminished neck looks too slender to sustain the enormous weight of the head. The nose and beard have been broken off by fanatics, and the red hue that formerly enlivened the features is almost wholly effaced. And yet, notwithstanding its fallen fortunes, the monster preserves an expression of sovereign strength and greatness. The eyes gaze out afar with a look of intense and profound thoughtfulness; the mouth still wears a smile; the whole countenance is informed with power and repose.

Suben. The goddess of childbirth, akin to the Greek Eileithyia and the Latin Lucin. She was worshiped in southern Egypt, where a city, Eileithyia, was consecrated to her. The goddess of childbirth in northern Egypt was called Nati, or Buto. The emblem of Suben was a vulture.

Thoth, or Tahut. He was one of the most popular of the Egyptian divinities, and would seem to have owed his origin to a confusion between two animal gods in prehistoric times: an ibis-headed god and an ape-headed god (cynocephalus), who were both lunar deities. The worship of Thoth-ibis was predominant in Lower Egypt; that of Thoth-cynocephalus in Upper Egypt and in Nubia. The principal center of his worship was at Unu, the Greek Hermopolis. The Hermopolitan theologians represented him as a universal miracle-worker. When the myth of Osiris was fully developed, Thoth entered into it as a secondary personage, became counselor and secretary of state to Osiris when the latter ruled over Egypt, and, when Osiris was slain by Set, aided Isis in preserving Horus from his enemies. It was greatly owing to the power of his magic incantations that the resurrection of Osiris was effected. It was his skill in magic that led the Greeks to identify him with Hermes. He also represented the divine intelligence or wisdom, and was called the "scribe of the gods." He invented writing, and taught men mathematics and other sciences and arts; he measured the floods of the Nile, and observed the course of the moon and the stars: the half disk on his head is that of the moon, the measurer of time. It is not easy to guess why he should have been given the head of an ibis, but he is almost always represented with it: in some pictures the ibis head is surmounted by a disk and plume, and he writes on tablets; in others he has no head-gear, and holds the nilometer with which he measured the rise of the Nile at flood-time. Among the magnificent wall pictures in the temple of Amon at Karnak is one in which he weighs the bags of gold dust, the gold ingots, the electrum bricks, and the ivory tusks brought as tribute from Punt (Somali) to Queen Hatasu. Thoth was the secretary of Osiris in the underworld. Also, when Set entered the tribunal of the gods, and charged that the birth of Horus was not stainless, the son of Isis owed his triumphant vindication to the eloquent defense of Thoth, the god of literature.

PART III

GRECIAN MYTHOLOGY

Acheloüs and Hercules. The river-god Acheloüs told the story of Erisichthon to Theseus and his companions, whom he was entertaining while they were delayed on their journey by the overflow of his waters. Having finished his story, he added: "But why should I tell of other persons' transformations, when I myself am an instance of the possession of this power? Sometimes I become a serpent, and sometimes a bull, with horns on my head. Or I should say, I once could do so; but now I have but one horn, having lost one." And here he groaned and was silent.

Theseus asked him the cause of his grief, and how he lost his horn. To which question the river-god replied: "Who likes to tell of his defeats? Yet I will not hesitate to relate mine, comforting myself with the thought of the greatness of my conqueror, for it was Hercules. Perhaps you have heard of the fame of Dejanira, the fairest of maidens, whom a host of suitors strove to win. Hercules and I were of the number, and the rest yielded to us two. He urged in his behalf his descent from Jove, and his labors by which he had exceeded the exactions of Juno, his stepmother. I, on the other hand, said to the father of the maiden, 'Behold me, the king of the waters that flow through your land. I am no stranger from a foreign shore, but belong to the country, a part of your realm. Let it not stand in my way that royal Juno owes me no enmity, nor punishes me with heavy tasks. As for this man, who boasts himself the son of Jove, it is either a false pretense, or disgraceful to him if true, for it cannot be true except by his mother's shame.' As I said this Hercules scowled upon me, and with difficulty restrained his rage. 'My hand will answer better than my tongue,' said he. 'I yield you the victory in words, but trust my cause to the strife of deeds.' With that he advanced toward me, and I was ashamed, after what I had said, to yield. I threw off my green vesture, and presented

69

myself for the struggle. He tried to throw me, now attacking my head, now my body. My bulk was my protection, and he assailed me in vain. For a time we stopped, then returned to the conflict. We each kept our position, determined not to yield, foot to foot, I bending over him, clenching his hands in mine, with my forehead almost touching his. Thrice Hercules tried to throw me off, and the fourth time he succeeded, brought me to the ground and himself upon my back. I tell you the truth, it was as if a mountain had fallen on me. I struggled to get my arms at liberty, panting and reeking with perspiration. He gave me no chance to recover, but seized my throat. My knees were on the earth and my mouth in the dust.

"Finding that I was no match for him in the warrior's art, I resorted to others, and glided away in the form of a serpent. I curled my body in a coil, and hissed at him with my forked tongue. He smiled scornfully at this, and said, 'It was the labor of my infancy to conquer snakes.' So saying he clasped my neck with his hands. I was almost choked, and struggled to get my neck out of his grasp. Vanquished in this form, I tried what alone remained to me, and assumed the form of a bull. He grasped my neck with his arm, and dragging my head down to the ground, overthrew me on the sand. Nor was this enough. His ruthless hand rent my horn from my head. The Naiades took it, consecrated it, and filled it with fragrant flowers. Plenty adopted my horn and made it her own, and called it Cornucopia."

The ancients explain this fight of Acheloüs with Hercules by saying: Acheloüs was a river that in seasons of rain overflowed its banks. When the fable says that Acheloüs loved Dejanira, and sought a union with her, the meaning is that the river in its windings flowed through part of Dejanira's kingdom. It was said to take the form of a snake because of its winding, and of a bull because it made a brawling or roaring in its course. When the river swelled, it made itself another channel. Thus its head was horned. Hercules prevented the return of these periodical overflows, by embankments and canals; and therefore he was said to have vanquished the river-god and cut off his horn. Finally, the lands formerly subject to overflow, but now redeemed, became very fertile, and this is meant by the horn of plenty.

There is another account of the origin of the Cornucopia. Jupiter at his birth was committed by his mother Rhea to the care of the daughters of Melisseus, a Cretan king. They fed the infant deity with the milk of the goat Amalthea. Jupiter broke off one of the horns of the goat and gave it to his nurses, and endowed it with the wonderful power of becoming filled with whatever the possessor might wish.

Actæon. It was midday when young Actæon, son of King Cadmus, thus addressed the youths who with him were hunting the stag in the mountains: "Friends, our nets and our weapons are wet with the blood of our victims; we have had sport enough for one day, and to-morrow we can renew our labors. Now, while Phœbus parches the earth, let us put by our implements and indulge ourselves with rest." There was a valley thick enclosed with cypresses and pines, sacred to the huntress queen, Diana. In the extremity of the valley was a cave. A fountain burst out from one side, whose open basin was bounded by a grassy rim. Here Diana, the goddess of the woods, used to come when weary with hunting and lave her virgin limbs in the sparkling water. One day, having repaired thither with her nymphs, she handed her javelin, her quiver, and her bow to one, her robe to another, while a third unbound the sandals from her feet. Then Crocale, the most skilful of them, arranged her hair, and Nephele, Hyale, and the rest drew water in capacious urns. While the goddess was thus employed in the labors of the toilet, behold Actæon, having quitted his companions, and rambling without any especial object, came to the place. As he presented himself at the entrance of the cave, the nymphs, seeing a man, screamed and rushed toward the goddess to hide her with their bodies. But she was taller than the rest and overtopped them all by a head. Such a color as tinges the clouds at sunset or at dawn came over the countenance of Diana, thus taken by surprise. Surrounded as she was by her nymphs, she yet turned half away, and sought with a sudden impulse for her arrows. As they were not at hand, she dashed the water into the face of the intruder, adding these words: "Now go and tell, if you can, that you have seen Diana unappareled." Immediately a pair of branching stag's horns grew out of his head, his neck gained in length, his ears grew sharp-pointed, his hands became feet, his arms long legs, his body was covered with a hairy spotted hide. Fear took the place of his former boldness, and the hero fled. What shall he do?—go home to seek the palace, or lie hid in the woods? The latter he was afraid, the former he was ashamed, to do. While he hesitated the dogs saw him. First Melampus, a Spartan dog, gave the signal with his bark, then Pamphagus, Dorceus, Lelaps, Theron, Nape, Tigris, and all the rest rushed after him swifter than the wind. Over rocks and cliffs, through mountain gorges that seemed impracticable, he fled and they followed. Where he had often chased the stag and cheered on his pack, his pack now chased him, cheered on by his huntsmen. He longed to cry out, "I am Actæon!" but the words came not at his will. Presently one dog fastened on his back, another seized his shoulder. While they held their master, the rest of the pack came up and buried their teeth in his flesh. His friends and fellow huntsmen cheered on the dogs, and looked everywhere for Actæon, calling on him to join the sport. At the sound of his name, he turned his head, and heard them regret that he should be away. It was not till the dogs had torn his life out that the anger of Diana was satisfied.

Admetus and **Alcestis.** Æsculapius, the son of Apollo, was endowed by his father with such skill in the healing art that he even restored the dead to life. At this Pluto took alarm, and prevailed on Jupiter to launch a thunderbolt at Æsculapius. Apollo was indignant at the destruction of his son, and wreaked his vengeance on the innocent workmen who had made the thunderbolt. These were the Cyclopes, who have their workshop under Mount Ætna, from which the smoke and flames of their furnaces are constantly issuing. Apollo shot his arrows at the Cyclopes, which so incensed Jupiter that he condemned him as a punishment to become the servant of a mortal for the space of one year. Accordingly Apollo went into the service of Admetus, King of Thessaly, and pastured his flocks for him on the banks of the river Amphrysos.

Admetus was a suitor, with others, for the hand of Alcestis, the daughter of Pelias, who promised her to him who should come for her in a chariot drawn by lions and boars. This task Admetus performed by the assistance of his divine herdsman, and was made happy in the possession of Alcestis. But Admetus fell ill; and when he was near to death, Apollo prevailed on the Fates to spare him on condition that some one would consent to die in his stead. Admetus, in his joy at this reprieve, thought little of the ransom, and, perhaps remembering the declarations of attachment which he had often heard from his courtiers and dependents, fancied that it would be easy to find a substitute. But it was not so. Brave warriors, who would

I shall have sung my death-song, and my harp-strings shall have ceased to vibrate, then I will bid farewell to life, and yield uncomplaining to my fate." This prayer, like the others, would have been unheeded, but to hear so famous a musician moved their rude hearts. "Suffer me," he added, "to arrange my dress. Apollo will not favor me unless I be clad in my minstrel garb."

He clothed his well-proportioned limbs in gold and purple fair to see; his tunic fell around him in graceful folds, jewels adorned his arms, his brow was crowned with a golden wreath, and over his neck and shoulders flowed his hair perfumed with odors. His left hand held the lyre, his right the ivory wand with which he struck its chords. The seamen gazed with admiration. He strode forward to the vessel's side and looked down into the blue sea. Addressing his lyre, he sang: "Companion of my voice, come with me to the realm of shades. Though Cerberus may growl, we know the power of song can tame his rage. Ye heroes of Elysium, who have passed the darkling flood— ye happy souls, soon shall I join your band. Yet can ye relieve my grief? Alas, I leave my friend behind me. Thou who didst find thy Eurydice, and lose her again as soon as found; when she had vanished like a dream, how didst thou hate the cheerful light! I must away, but I will not fear. The gods look down upon me. Ye who slay me unoffending, when I am no more, your time of trembling shall come. Ye Nereids, receive your guest, who throws himself upon your mercy!" So saying, he sprang into the deep sea. The waves covered him, and the seamen held on their way, fancying themselves safe from all danger of detection.

But the strains of his music had drawn round him the inhabitants of the deep to listen, and Dolphins followed the ship as if chained by a spell. While he struggled in the waves, a Dolphin offered him his back, and carried him mounted thereon safe to shore. At the spot where he landed, a monument of brass was afterward erected upon the rocky shore.

When Arion and the Dolphin parted, each to his own element, Arion thus poured forth his thanks: "Farewell, thou faithful, friendly fish! Would that I could reward thee; but thou canst not wend with me, nor I with thee. Companionship we may not have. May Galatea, queen of the deep, accord thee her favor, and thou, proud of the burden, draw her chariot over the mirror of the sea."

Arion hastened from the shore, and soon saw the towers of Corinth.

He journeyed on, harp in hand, singing as he went, full of love and happiness, forgetting his losses, and mindful only of what remained, his friend and his lyre. He entered the hospitable halls, and was soon clasped in the embrace of Periander. "I come back to thee, my friend," he said. "The talent that a god bestowed has been the delight of thousands, but false knaves have stripped me of my well-earned treasure; yet I retain the consciousness of wide-spread fame." Then he told Periander all the wonderful events that had befallen him, who heard him with amazement. "Shall such wickedness triumph?" said he. "Then in vain is power lodged in my hands. That we may discover the criminals, you must remain here in concealment, and so they will approach without suspicion." When the ship arrived in the harbor, he summoned the mariners before him. "Have you heard anything of Arion?" he inquired. "I anxiously look for his return." They replied: "We left him well and prosperous in Tarentum." As they said these words, Arion stepped forth and faced them. His well-proportioned limbs were arrayed in gold and purple fair to see, his tunic fell around him in graceful folds, jewels adorned his arms, his brow was crowned with a golden wreath, and over his neck and shoulders flowed his hair perfumed with odors; his left hand held the lyre, his right the ivory wand with which he struck its chords. They fell prostrate at his feet, as if a lightning bolt had struck them. "We meant to murder him, and he has become a god. O Earth, open and receive us!" Then Periander spoke. "He lives, the master of the lay! Kind Heaven protects the poet's life. As for you, I invoke not the spirit of vengeance; Arion wishes not your blood. Ye slaves of avarice, begone! Seek some barbarous land, and never may aught beautiful delight your souls!"

Aristæus, the Bee-keeper. Aristæus, who first taught the management of bees, was a son of the water-nymph Cyrene. His bees had perished, and he resorted for aid to his mother. He stood at the riverside and thus addressed her: "O mother, the pride of my life is taken from me! I have lost my precious bees. My care and skill have availed me nothing, and you my mother have not warded off from me the blow of misfortune." His mother heard these complaints as she sat in her palace at the bottom of the river with her attendant nymphs around her. They were spinning and weaving, while one told stories to amuse the rest. The sad voice of Aristæus interrupting their occupation, one of them put her head above the water and, seeing him, returned and gave information to his mother, who ordered that he should be brought into her presence. The river at her command opened itself and let him pass in, while it stood curled like a mountain on either side. He descended to the region where the fountains of the great rivers lie; he saw the enormous receptacles of waters and was almost deafened with the roar while he surveyed them hurrying off in various directions to water the face of the earth. At his mother's apartments he was hospitably received by Cyrene and her nymphs, who spread their table with the richest dainties. They first poured out libations to Neptune, then regaled themselves with the feast, and after that Cyrene thus addressed him: "There is an old prophet named Proteus, who dwells in the sea and is a favorite of Neptune, whose herd of sea-calves he pastures. We nymphs hold him in great respect, for he is learned and knows all things, past, present, and to come. He can tell you, my son, the cause of the mortality among your bees, and how you may remedy it. But he will not do it voluntarily, however you may entreat him. You must compel him by force. If you seize him and chain him, he will answer your questions in order to get released, for he cannot by all his arts get away, if you hold fast the chains. I will take you to his cave, where he comes at noon to take his midday repose. Then you may easily secure him. But when he finds himself captured, his resort is to a power he possesses of changing himself into various forms. He will become a wild boar or a fierce tiger, a scaly dragon or lion with yellow mane. Or he will make a noise like the crackling of flames or the rush of water, so as to tempt you to let go the chain, when he will make his escape. But you have only to keep him fast bound, and at last when he finds all his arts unavailing, he will return to his own figure and obey your commands." So saying, she sprinkled her son with fragrant nectar, the beverage of the gods, and immediately an unusual vigor filled his frame and courage his heart, while perfume breathed all around him.

The nymph led her son to the prophet's cave and concealed him among the recesses of the rocks, while she herself took her place behind the clouds. When noon came and the hour when men and herds retreat from the glaring sun to indulge in quiet slumber, Proteus issued from the water, followed by his herd of sea-calves which spread themselves along the shore. He sat on the rock and counted his herd; then stretched himself on the floor of the cave and went to sleep. Aristæus hardly allowed him to get fairly asleep before he fixed the fetters on him and shouted aloud. Proteus, waking and finding himself captured, immediately resorted to his arts, becoming first a fire, then a flood, then a horrible wild beast, in rapid succession. But finding all would not do, he at last resumed his own form and addressed the youth in angry accents: "Who are you, bold youth, who thus invade my abode, and what do you want with me?" Aristæus replied: "Proteus, you know already, for it is needless for anyone to attempt to deceive you. And do you also cease your efforts to elude me. I am led hither by divine assistance, to know from you the cause of my misfortune and how to remedy it." At these words the prophet fixing on him his gray eyes, with a piercing look, thus spoke: "You receive the merited reward of your deeds, by which Eurydice met her death, for in flying from you she trod upon a serpent, of whose bite she died. To avenge her death, the nymphs, her companions, have sent this destruction to your bees. You have to appease their anger, and thus it must be done: Select four bulls, of perfect form and size, and four cows of equal beauty, build four altars to the nymphs, and sacrifice the animals, leaving their carcasses in the leafy grove. To Orpheus and Eurydice you shall pay such funeral honors as may allay their resentment. Returning after nine days you will examine the bodies of the cattle slain and see what will befall."

Aristæus faithfully obeyed these directions. He sacrificed the cattle, he left their bodies in the grove, he offered funeral honors to the shades of Orpheus and Eurydice; then returning on the ninth day he examined the bodies of the animals, and, wonderful to relate! a swarm of bees had taken possession of one of the carcasses and were pursuing their labors there as in a hive.

Atalanta. Atalanta's fortune had been told, and it was to this effect: "Atalanta, do not marry; marriage will be your ruin." Terrified by this oracle, she fled the society of men, and devoted herself to the sports of the chase. To all suitors (for she had many) she imposed a condition that was usually effectual in relieving her of their persecutions—"I will be the prize of him who shall conquer me in the race; but death must be the penalty of all who try and fail." In spite of this hard condition some would try. Hippomenes was to be judge of the race. "Can it be possible that any will be so rash as to risk so much for a wife?" said he. But when he saw her lay aside her robe for the race, he changed his mind, and said: "Pardon me, youths, I knew not the prize you were competing for." As he surveyed them, he wished them all to be beaten, and swelled with envy of anyone that seemed at all likely to win. As she ran she looked more beautiful than ever. The breezes seemed to give wings to her feet; her hair flew over her shoulders, and the gay fringe of her garment fluttered behind her. A ruddy hue tinged the whiteness of her skin, such as a crimson curtain casts on a marble wall. All her competitors were distanced and were put to death without mercy. Hippomenes, not daunted by this result, fixing his eyes on the virgin, said: "Why boast of beating those laggards? I offer myself for the contest." Atalanta looked at him with a pitying countenance, and hardly knew whether she would conquer him or not. "What god can tempt one so young and handsome to throw himself away? I pity him, not for his beauty (yet he is beautiful) but for his youth. I wish he would give up the race, or if he will be so mad, I hope he may outrun me." While she hesitated, revolving these thoughts, the spectators grew impatient for the race, and her father prompted her to prepare. Then Hippomenes addressed a prayer to Venus: "Help me, Venus, for you have led me on." Venus heard, and was propitious.

In the garden of her temple, in her own island of Cyprus, is a tree with yellow leaves and yellow branches and golden fruit. Hence she gathered three golden apples, and, unseen by anyone else, gave them to Hippomenes, and told him how to use them. The signal was given; each left the goal, and skimmed over the sand. The cries of the spectators cheered Hippomenes: "Now, now do your best! haste, haste! you gain on her! relax not! one more effort!" It was doubtful whether the youth or the maiden heard these cries with the greater pleasure. But his breath began to fail him, his throat was dry, the goal far off. At that moment he threw down one of the golden apples. The virgin was all amazement. She stopped to pick it up. Hippomenes shot ahead. Shouts burst forth from all sides. She redoubled her efforts, and soon overtook him. Again he threw an apple. She stopped again, but again came up with him. The goal was near; one chance only remained. "Now, goddess," said he, "prosper your gift!" and threw the last apple off at one side. She looked at it, and hesitated; Venus impelled her to turn aside for it. She did so, and was vanquished. The youth carried off his prize.

But the lovers were so full of their own happiness that they forgot to pay due honor to Venus; and the goddess was offended at their ingratitude. She caused them to give offense to Cybele. That powerful goddess was not to be insulted with impunity. She took from them their human form and turned them into animals of characters resembling their own: of the huntress-heroine, triumphing in the blood of her lovers, she made a lioness, and of her lord and master a lion, and yoked them to her car, where they are still to be seen in all representations, in statuary or painting, of the goddess Cybele.

Aurora and **Tithonus.** The goddess of the Dawn, like her sister the Moon, was at times inspired with the love of mortals. Her greatest favorite was Tithonus, son of Laomedon, King of Troy. She stole him away, and prevailed on Jupiter to grant him immortality; but she forgot to have youth joined in the gift, and after some time she began to discern, to her great mortification, that he was growing old. When his hair was quite white she left his society; but he still had the range of her palace, lived on ambrosial food, and was clad in celestial raiment. At last he lost the power of using his limbs, and then she shut him up in his chamber, whence his feeble voice might at times be heard. Finally she turned him into a grasshopper.

Memnon was the son of Aurora and Tithonus. He was King of the Ethiopians and dwelt in the extreme East, on the shore of the Ocean. He came with his warriors to assist the kindred of his father in the war of Troy. King Priam received him with great honors, and listened with admiration to his narrative of the wonders of the shore.

The very day after his arrival Memnon, impatient of repose, led his troops to the field. Antilochus, the brave son of Nestor, fell by his hand, and the Greeks were put to flight, when Achilles appeared and restored the battle. A long and doubtful contest ensued between him and the son of Aurora; at last victory declared for Achilles, Memnon fell, and the Trojans fled in dismay.

Aurora, who from her station in the sky had viewed with apprehension the danger of her son, when she saw him fall directed his brothers the Winds to convey his body to the banks of the river Esepus in Paphlagonia. In the evening Aurora came, accompanied by the Hours and the Pleiads, and wept and lamented over her son. Night, in sympathy with her grief, spread the heaven with clouds;

all nature mourned for the offspring of the Dawn. The Ethiopians raised his tomb on the banks of the stream in the grove of the Nymphs, and Jupiter caused the sparks and cinders of his funeral pile to be turned into birds, which, dividing into two flocks, fought over the pile till they fell into the flame. Every year at the anniversary of his death they return and celebrate his obsequies in like manner. Aurora remains inconsolable for the loss of her son. Her tears still flow, and may be seen at early morning in the form of dew-drops on the grass.

Bacchus. Bacchus was the son of Jupiter and Semele. Juno, to gratify her resentment against Semele, contrived a plan for her destruction. Assuming the form of Beroë, Semele's aged nurse, she insinuated doubts whether it was indeed Jove himself who came as a lover. Heaving a sigh, she said: "I hope it will turn out so, but I can't help being afraid. People are not always what they pretend to be. If he is indeed Jove, make him give some proof of it. Ask him to come arrayed in all his splendors, such as he wears in heaven. That will put the matter beyond a doubt." Semele was persuaded to make the experiment. She asked a favor without naming what it was. Jove gave his promise, and confirmed it with the irrevocable oath, attesting the river Styx. Then she made known her request. The god would have stopped her as she spoke, but she was too quick for him. The words escaped, and he could unsay neither his promise nor her request. In deep distress he left her and returned to the upper regions. There he clothed himself in his splendors, not putting on all his terrors, as when he overthrew the giants, but what was known among the gods as his lesser panoply. Arrayed in this, he entered the chamber of Semele. Her mortal frame could not endure the splendors of the immortal radiance and she was consumed to ashes.

Jove took the infant Bacchus and gave him in charge to the Nysæan nymphs, who nourished his infancy and childhood, and for their care were rewarded by Jupiter by being placed, at the Hyades, among the stars. When Bacchus grew up he discovered the culture of the vine and the mode of extracting its juice; but Juno struck him with madness, and drove him forth a wanderer through the earth. In Phrygia the goddess Rhea cured him and taught him her religious rites, and he set out on a progress through Asia, teaching the people the cultivation of the vine. The most famous part of his wanderings is his expedition to India, which lasted several years.

Returning in triumph, he undertook to introduce his worship into Greece, but was opposed by some princes who dreaded its introduction on account of the disorders and madness it brought with it. As he approached his native city Thebes, Pentheus the King, who had no respect for the new worship, forbade its rites to be performed. But when it was known that Bacchus was advancing, men and women, chiefly the latter, young and old, poured forth to meet him and to join his triumphal march.

In vain Pentheus remonstrated, commanded, and threatened. "Go," said he to his attendants, "seize this vagabond leader of the rout and bring him to me. I will soon make him confess his false claim of heavenly parentage and renounce his counterfeit worship." In vain his nearest friends and wisest counselors remonstrated and begged him not to oppose the god; their remonstrances only made him more violent.

But now the attendants returned whom he had despatched to seize Bacchus. They had been driven away by the Bacchanals, but had succeeded in taking one of them prisoner, whom, with his hands tied behind him, they brought before the King. Pentheus beholding him with wrathful countenance said: "Fellow! you shall speedily be put to death, that your fate may be a warning to others; but though I grudge the delay of your punishment, speak, tell us who you are, and what are these new rites you presume to celebrate?"

The prisoner unterrified responded: "My name is Acetes; my country is Mæonia; my parents were poor and had no fields or flocks to leave me, but they left me their fishing-rods and nets and their fisherman's trade. This I followed for some time, till, growing weary of remaining in one place, I learned the pilot's art and how to guide my course by the stars. It happened, as I was sailing for Delos, we touched at the island of Dia and went ashore. Next morning I sent the men for fresh water while I mounted the hill to observe the wind; when my men returned bringing with them a prize, as they thought, a boy of delicate appearance, whom they had found asleep. They judged he was a noble youth, perhaps a king's son, and they might get a liberal ransom for him. I observed his dress, his walk, his face. There was something in them which I felt sure was more than mortal. I said to my men: 'What god is concealed in that form I know not, but some one there certainly is. Pardon us, gentle deity, for the violence we have done you, and give success to our undertakings.'

battle of the Lapithæ and Centaurs, a favorite subject with the sculptors and poets of antiquity.

But not all the Centaurs were like the rude guests of Pirithous. Chiron was instructed by Apollo and Diana, and was renowned for his skill in hunting, medicine, music, and the art of prophecy. The most distinguished heroes of Grecian story were his pupils. Among the rest the infant Æsculapius was entrusted to his charge, by Apollo, his father. When the sage returned to his home bearing the infant his daughter Ocyroe came forth to meet him, and at sight of the child burst forth into a prophetic strain (for she was a prophetess), foretelling the glory that he was to achieve. Æsculapius became a renowned physician, and even in one instance restored the dead to life. Pluto resented this, and Jupiter, at his request, struck the bold physician with lightning and killed him, but after his death received him into the number of the gods.

Chiron was the wisest and justest of all the Centaurs, and at his death Jupiter placed him among the stars as the constellation Sagittarius.

Cephalus and **Procris.** Cephalus was a beautiful youth and fond of manly sports. He would rise before the dawn to pursue the chase. Aurora saw him when she first looked forth, fell in love with him, and stole him away. But Cephalus was just married to a charming wife whom he devotedly loved. Her name was Procris. She was a favorite of Diana, the goddess of hunting, who had given her a dog that could outrun every rival, and a javelin that never would fail of its mark; and Procris gave these presents to her husband. Cephalus was so happy in his wife that he resisted all the entreaties of Aurora, and she finally dismissed him in displeasure, saying: "Go, ungrateful mortal, keep your wife, whom, if I am not much mistaken, you will one day be very sorry you ever saw again." Cephalus returned, and was as happy as ever in his wife and his woodland sports.

It happened that some angry deity had sent a ravenous fox to annoy the country; and the hunters turned out in great strength to capture it. Their efforts were all in vain; no dog could run it down; and at last they came to Cephalus to borrow his famous dog, whose name was Lelaps. No sooner was the dog let loose than he darted off, quicker than their eye could follow him. If they had not seen his footprints in the sand they would have thought he flew.

Cephalus and others stood on a hill and saw the race. The fox tried every art; he ran in a circle and turned on his track, the dog close upon him, with open jaws, snapping at his heels, but biting only the air. Cephalus was about to use his javelin when suddenly he saw both dog and game stop instantly. The heavenly powers who had given both were not willing that either should conquer. In the very attitude of life and action they were turned into stone. So lifelike and natural did they look, you would have thought that one was about to bark, the other to leap forward.

Cephalus, though he had lost his dog, still continued to take delight in the chase. He would go out at early morning, ranging the woods and hills unaccompanied by anyone. Sometimes he would say aloud: "Come, sweet breeze, come and fan my breast, come and allay the heat that burns me." Someone passing by one day heard him talking in this way to the air, and, foolishly believing that he was talking to some maiden, went and told the secret to Procris, Cephalus's wife. At the sudden shock she fainted away. But presently recovering, she said: "It cannot be true; I will not believe it unless I myself am a witness to it." So she waited, with anxious heart, till the next morning, when Cephalus went to hunt as usual. Then she stole out after him, and concealed herself in the place where the informer directed her. Cephalus came as he was wont when tired with sport, and stretched himself on the green bank, saying: "Come, sweet breeze, come and fan me; you know how I love you! you make the groves and my solitary rambles delightful." He was running on in this way when he heard, or thought he heard, a sound as of a sob in the bushes. Supposing it some wild animal, he threw his javelin at the spot. A cry from his beloved Procris told him that the weapon had too surely met its mark. He rushed to the place, and found her bleeding, and with sinking strength endeavoring to draw forth from the wound the javelin, her own gift. Cephalus raised her from the earth, strove to stanch the blood, and called her to revive and not to leave him miserable, to reproach himself with her death. She opened her feeble eyes, and forced herself to utter these few words: "I implore you, if you have ever loved me, if I have ever deserved kindness at your hands, my husband, grant me this last request: do not marry that odious Breeze!" This disclosed the whole mystery; but alas! what advantage to disclose it now? She died; but her face wore a calm expression, and she

looked pityingly and forgivingly on her husband when he explained
and made her understand the truth.

Clytie. Clytie was a water-nymph and in love with Apollo,
who made her no return. So she pined away, sitting all day long
upon the cold ground, with her unbound tresses streaming over
her shoulders. Nine days she sat and tasted neither food nor drink,
her own tears and the chilly dew her only food. She gazed on the
sun when he rose, and as he passed through his daily course to his
setting; she saw no other object, her face turned constantly on him.
At last, they say, her limbs rooted in the ground, and her face became a flower, which turns on its stem so as always to face the sun
throughout its daily course; for it retains to that extent the feeling
of the nymph from whom it sprang.

Cupid and **Psyche.** A certain king and queen had three daughters. The charms of the two elder were more than common, but
the beauty of the youngest, Psyche, was so wonderful that words
cannot express its due praise. The fame of her beauty was so great
that strangers from neighboring countries came in crowds to enjoy
the sight. In fact, Venus found her altars deserted, while men turned
their devotion to that young virgin. This gave great offense to Venus.
Thereupon she called her winged son Cupid, pointed out Psyche
to him, and said: "My dear son, punish that contumacious beauty;
give thy mother a revenge as sweet as her injuries are great; infuse
into the bosom of that haughty girl a passion for some low, mean,
unworthy being, so that she may reap a mortification as great as her
present exultation and triumph."

There are two fountains in Venus's garden, one of sweet waters,
the other of bitter. Cupid filled two amber vases, one from each
fountain, and suspending them from the top of his quiver, hastened
to the chamber of Psyche, whom he found asleep. He shed a few
drops from the bitter fountain over her lips, though the sight of her
almost moved him to pity; then touched her side with the point
of his arrow. At the touch she awoke, and opened eyes upon Cupid
(himself invisible), which so startled him that in his confusion he
wounded himself with his own arrow. Heedless of his wound, his
whole thought now was to repair the mischief he had done, and he
poured the balmy drops of joy over all her silken ringlets.

Psyche, henceforth frowned upon by Venus, derived no benefit from
all her charms. True, all eyes were cast eagerly upon her, and every

mouth spoke her praises; but neither king, royal youth, nor plebeian presented himself to demand her in marriage. Her two elder sisters were married to royal princes; but Psyche, in her lonely apartment, deplored her solitude, sick of her own beauty.

Her parents consulted the oracle of Apollo, and received this answer: "The virgin is destined to be the bride of no mortal lover. Her future husband awaits her on the top of the mountain. He is a monster whom neither gods nor men can resist." This filled all the people with dismay, and her parents abandoned themselves to grief. But Psyche said: "Why, my dear parents, do you now lament me? You should rather have grieved when the people showered upon me undeserved honors, and with one voice called me a Venus. I now perceive that I am a victim to that name. I submit. Lead me to that rock to which my unhappy fate has destined me." Accordingly, the royal maid took her place in the procession, and with her parents, amid the lamentations of the people, ascended the mountain, on the summit of which they left her alone.

While Psyche stood on the ridge of the mountain, the gentle Zephyr bore her with an easy motion into a flowery dale. By degrees her mind became composed, and she laid herself down on the grassy bank to sleep. When she awoke refreshed with sleep, she looked round and beheld a pleasant grove of tall and stately trees. She entered it, and in the midst discovered a fountain, sending forth crystal waters, and a magnificent palace whose august front impressed the spectator that it was not the work of mortal hands. She approached the building and entered. Golden pillars supported the vaulted roof, and the walls were enriched with carvings and paintings representing beasts of the chase and rural scenes. Besides the apartments of state there were others filled with all manner of treasures, and beautiful and precious productions of nature and art.

A voice addressed her, though she saw no one, uttering these words: "Sovereign lady, all that you see is yours. We whose voices you hear are your servants and shall obey all your commands with our utmost care and diligence. Retire therefore to your chamber and repose on your bed of down, and when you see fit repair to the bath. Supper awaits you in the adjoining alcove when it pleases you to take your seat there."

After repose and the refreshment of the bath, Psyche seated herself in the alcove, where a table immediately presented itself, without any visible aid from waiters or servants, covered with delicate food and choice wines. There was also music by invisible performers.

She had not yet seen her destined husband. He came only in the hours of darkness, and fled before the dawn of morning, but his accents were full of love, and inspired a like passion in her. She often asked him to stay and let her behold him, but he would not consent. "Why should you wish to behold me?" he said; "have you any doubt of my love? I would rather you would love me as an equal than adore me as a god." But one night she gained his consent that her sisters might be brought to see her.

Zephyr conducted them thither. "Come," said Psyche, "enter my house and refresh yourselves." Taking their hands, she led them into her golden palace, and committed them to the care of her train of attendant voices.

They asked numberless questions, among others what sort of person her husband was. Psyche replied that he was a beautiful youth, who usually spent the daytime in hunting. Not satisfied with this reply, they soon made her confess that she never had seen him. Then they proceeded to fill her bosom with dark suspicions. "Call to mind," they said, "the Pythian oracle that declared you destined to marry a direful monster. The inhabitants of this valley say that your husband is a terrible serpent, who nourishes you for a while with dainties that he may by and by devour you. Take our advice. Provide yourself with a lamp and a sharp knife; put them in concealment, and when he is sound asleep, slip out of bed, bring forth your lamp and see for yourself whether what they say is true. If it is, hesitate not to cut off the monster's head, and thereby recover your liberty."

So Psyche prepared her lamp and a sharp knife, and hid them. When he had fallen into his first sleep, she silently rose and uncovering her lamp beheld, not a hideous monster, but the most beautiful and charming of the gods, with golden ringlets wandering over his snowy neck and crimson cheek, with two dewy wings on his shoulders, whiter than snow, and with shining feathers like the tender blossoms of spring. As she leaned the lamp over to have a nearer view of his face a drop of burning oil fell on the shoulder of the god, startled with which he opened his eyes and fixed them full upon her; then, without saying one word, he spread his white wings and flew out of the window. Psyche, in vain endeavoring to follow him, fell from the window to the ground.   Cupid, beholding her as she lay in the dust, stopped his flight for an instant and said: "O foolish Psyche, is it thus you repay my love?   After I have disobeyed my mother's commands and made you my wife, will you think me a monster and cut off my head?   But go; return to your sisters, whose advice you seem to think preferable to mine.   I inflict no other punishment on you than to leave you forever.   Love cannot dwell with suspicion."   So saying, he fled away.

When she had recovered some degree of composure she looked around, but the palace and gardens had vanished, and she found herself in the open field not far from the city where her sisters dwelt. She repaired thither and told them the whole story of her misfortunes, at which, pretending to grieve, those spiteful creatures inwardly rejoiced; "for now," said they, "he will perhaps choose one of us." With this idea, without saying a word of her intentions, each of them rose early the next morning and ascended the mountain, and having reached the top, called upon Zephyr to receive her and bear her to his lord; then leaping up, and not being sustained by Zephyr, fell down the precipice and was dashed to pieces.

By the advice of Ceres, Psyche went to the temple of Venus and sought to be reconciled with that goddess.   "Most undutiful and faithless of servants," said Venus, "do you at last remember that you really have a mistress?   Or have you rather come to see your sick husband, still laid up of the wound given him by his loving wife? You are so ill-favored and disagreeable that the only way you can merit your lover must be by dint of industry and diligence.   I will make trial of your housewifery."   Then she ordered Psyche to be led to the storehouse of her temple, where was a great quantity of wheat, barley, millet, vetches, beans, and lentils prepared for food for her pigeons, and said: "Separate all these grains, putting all of the same kind in a parcel by themselves, and see that you get it done before evening."

Psyche, in consternation at the enormous work, sat stupid and silent, without moving a finger.   While she sat despairing, Cupid stirred up the little ant, a native of the fields, to take compassion on her.   The leader of the ant-hill, followed by hosts of his six-legged subjects, approached the heap, and taking grain by grain, they separated the pile, sorting each kind to its parcel; and when it was done, they vanished in a moment.

Venus, at twilight, returned, and seeing the task done, exclaimed: "This is no work of yours, wicked one, but his, whom to your own and his misfortune you have enticed." So saying, she threw her a piece of black bread for her supper and went away.

Next morning Venus ordered Psyche to be called, and said to her: "Behold yonder grove which stretches along the margin of the water. There you will find sheep feeding without a shepherd, with golden-shining fleeces on their backs. Go, fetch me a sample of that precious wool gathered from every one of their fleeces." Psyche went to the riverside, where the river-god told her how she could safely get the wool, and she soon returned to Venus with her arms full of the golden fleece. "I know very well it is by none of your own doings," said Venus, "that you have succeeded in this task, and I am not yet satisfied that you have any capacity to make yourself useful. But I have another task for you. Go your way to the infernal shades, and give this box to Proserpine and say: 'My mistress Venus desires you to send her a little of your beauty, for in tending her sick son she has lost some of her own.'"

Psyche, satisfied that her destruction was at hand, went to the top of a high tower to precipitate herself headlong, thus to take the shortest way to the shades below. But a voice from the tower told her how by a certain cave she might reach the realms of Pluto, and how to avoid all the dangers of the road. But the voice added: "When Proserpine has given you the box, filled with her beauty, of all things this is chiefly to be observed by you, that you never open or look into the box, nor allow your curiosity to pry into the treasure of the beauty of the goddesses."

Psyche, encouraged by this advice, obeyed it in all things, and performed the errand in safety. But as she was returning a desire seized her to examine the contents of the box. "What," said she, "shall I, the carrier of this divine beauty, not take the least bit to put on my cheeks to appear to more advantage in the eyes of my beloved husband?" She carefully opened the box, but found nothing there of any beauty at all, only an infernal and truly Stygian sleep, which, being thus set free, took possession of her, and she fell in the midst of the road, a sleepy body without sense or motion.

But Cupid, being now recovered from his wound, and not able longer to bear the absence of his beloved Psyche, slipping through the smallest crack of the window of his chamber which happened to be left open, flew to the spot where Psyche lay, and gathering up the sleep from her body, closed it again in the box, and waked Psyche with a light touch of one of his arrows. "Again," said he, "hast thou almost perished by the same curiosity. But now perform exactly the task imposed on you by my mother, and I will take care of the rest." Then Cupid, as swift as lightning penetrating the heights of heaven, presented himself before Jupiter with his supplication. Jupiter pleaded the cause of the lovers so earnestly with Venus that he won her consent. On this he sent Mercury to bring Psyche up to the heavenly assembly, and when she arrived, handing her a cup of ambrosia, he said: "Drink this, Psyche, and be immortal; nor shall Cupid ever break away from the knot in which he is tied, but these nuptials shall be perpetual." Thus Psyche became at last united to Cupid, and in due time a daughter was born to them, whose name was Pleasure.

Dædalus. The labyrinth from which Theseus escaped by means of Ariadne's clue was built by Dædalus, a most skilful artificer. It was an edifice with numberless winding passages and turnings opening into one another, and seemed to have neither beginning nor end, like the river Mæander, which returns on itself, and flows now onward, now backward, in its course to the sea. Dædalus built the labyrinth for King Minos, but afterward lost the favor of the King and was shut up in a tower. He contrived to make his escape from his prison, but could not leave the island by sea, as the King kept strict watch on all the vessels, and permitted none to sail without being carefully searched. "Minos may control the land and sea," said Dædalus, "but not the regions of the air. I will try that way." So he set to work to fabricate wings for himself and his young son Icarus. He wrought feathers together, beginning with the smallest and adding larger, so as to form an increasing surface. The larger ones he secured with thread and the smaller with wax, and gave the whole a gentle curvature like the wings of a bird. Icarus, the boy, stood and looked on, sometimes running to gather up the feathers which the wind had blown away, and then handling the wax and working it over with his fingers, by his play impeding his father in his labors. When at last his work was done, the artist, waving his wings, found himself buoyed upward and hung suspended, poising himself on the beaten air. He next equipped his son in the same manner, and taught him how to fly. When all was prepared for

from the chasm, uttered a pleasing murmur." Thus Acis was changed into a river, and the river retains the name of Acis.

Glaucus and **Scylla.** Glaucus was a fisherman. One day he had drawn his nets to land, and had taken a great many fishes. So he emptied his net, and proceeded to sort the fishes on the grass. The place where he stood was a beautiful island in the river, a solitary spot. On a sudden, the fishes began to revive and move their fins as if they were in the water; and while he looked on astonished, they moved to the water, plunged in, and swam away. "What herb has such power?" he exclaimed; and gathering some of it, he tasted it. Hardly had the juices of the plant reached his palate when he found himself agitated with a desire for the water, and bidding farewell to earth, he plunged into the stream. The gods of the water received him graciously, and obtained the consent of Oceanus and Tethys that all that was mortal in him should be washed away. A hundred rivers poured their waters over him. Then he lost consciousness, and when he recovered he found himself changed in form and mind. His hair was sea-green, and trailed behind him on the water; his shoulders grew broad, and what had been thighs and legs assumed the form of a fish's tail. The sea-gods complimented him on the change of his appearance, and he fancied himself rather a good-looking person.

One day Glaucus saw the beautiful maiden Scylla, the favorite of the water-nymphs, rambling on the shore, and, when she had found a sheltered nook, laving her limbs in the clear water. He fell in love with her, and showing himself on the surface, spoke to her. She turned to run immediately on the sight of him, and ran till she had gained a cliff overlooking the sea. Here she turned to see whether it was a god or a sea animal, and observed with wonder his shape and color. Glaucus, partly emerging from the water, and supporting himself against a rock, said: "Maiden, I am no monster, nor a sea animal, but a god; and neither Proteus nor Triton ranks higher than I. Once I was a mortal, and followed the sea for a living; but now I belong wholly to it." Then he told the story of his metamorphosis, and how he had been promoted to his present dignity, and added, "But what avails all this if it fails to move your heart?" Scylla turned and hastened away.

Glaucus was in despair, but it occurred to him to consult the enchantress, Circe, to whom he said: "Goddess, I entreat your pity.

I love Scylla. I am ashamed to tell you how I have sued and promised to her, and how scornfully she has treated me. I beseech you to use your incantations, or potent herbs, if they are more prevailing, not to cure me of my love, for that I do not wish, but to make her share it and yield me a like return." To which Circe replied: "You had better pursue a willing object; you are worthy to be sought, instead of having to seek in vain. Be not diffident, know your own worth. I protest to you that even I, goddess though I be, and learned in the virtues of plants and spells, should not know how to refuse you. If she scorns you, scorn her; meet one who is ready to meet you half-way, and thus make a due return to both at once." To these words Glaucus replied: "Sooner shall trees grow at the bottom of the ocean, and seaweed on the top of the mountains, than I will cease to love Scylla, and her alone."

The goddess was indignant, but she liked him well; so she turned her wrath against poor Scylla. She took plants of poisonous powers and mixed them together, with incantations and charms. Then she passed through the crowd of gamboling beasts, the victims of her art, and proceeded to the coast of Sicily, where Scylla lived. There was a little bay on the shore to which Scylla used to resort, in the heat of the day, to breathe the air of the sea and to bathe in its waters. Here the goddess poured her poisonous mixture, and muttered over it incantations of mighty power. Scylla came as usual and plunged into the water up to her waist. What was her horror to perceive a brood of serpents and barking monsters surrounding her! At first she could not imagine they were a part of herself, and tried to run from them, and to drive them away; but as she ran she carried them with her, and when she tried to touch her limbs she found her hands touch only the yawning jaws of monsters. Scylla remained rooted to the spot. Her temper grew as ugly as her form, and she took pleasure in devouring hapless mariners who came within her grasp. Thus she destroyed six of the companions of Ulysses, and tried to wreck the ships of Æneas, till at last she was turned into a rock, and as such still continues to be a terror to mariners.

The Golden Fleece. In very ancient times a king and queen named Athamas and Nephele lived in Thessaly. They had two children, a boy and a girl. After a time Athamas grew indifferent to his wife, put her away, and took another. Nephele suspected danger to her children from the influence of the stepmother, and took measures to send them out of her reach. Mercury assisted her, and gave her a ram, with a golden fleece, on which she set the two children, trusting that the ram would convey them to a place of safety. The ram vaulted into the air with the children on his back, taking his course to the East. When crossing the strait that divides Europe and Asia, the girl, whose name was Helle, fell into the sea, which from her was called Hellespont—now the Dardanelles. The ram continued his career till he reached the kingdom of Colchis, on the eastern shore of the Black Sea, where he safely landed the boy Phryxus, who was hospitably received by Æetes, king of the country. Phryxus sacrificed the ram to Jupiter, and gave the golden fleece to Æetes, who placed it in a consecrated grove, under the care of a sleepless dragon.

There was another kingdom in Thessaly near to that of Athamas, ruled over by a relative of his. The King, Æson, being tired of the cares of government, surrendered his crown to his brother Pelias, on condition that he should hold it only during the minority of Jason, the son of Æson. When Jason was grown up and came to demand the crown from his uncle, Pelias pretended to be willing to yield it, but at the same time suggested to the young man the glorious adventure of going in quest of the golden fleece, which it was well known was in the kingdom of Colchis, and was, as Pelias pretended, the rightful property of their family. Jason forthwith made preparations for the expedition. At that time the only species of navigation known to the Greeks consisted of small boats or canoes hollowed out from trunks of trees, so that when Jason employed Argus to build him a vessel capable of containing fifty men it was considered a gigantic undertaking. It was accomplished, however, and the vessel was named Argo, from the name of the builder. Jason sent his invitation to all the adventurous young men of Greece, and soon found himself at the head of a band of bold youths, many of whom afterward were renowned among the heroes and demigods of Greece. Hercules, Theseus, Orpheus, and Nestor were among them. They are called the Argonauts, from the name of their vessel.

The Argo left the shores of Thessaly, and having touched at the island of Lemnos, crossed to Mysia, and thence to Thrace. Here they found the sage Phineus, and from him received instruction as to their future course. The entrance of the Euxine Sea was impeded by two small rocky islands, which floated on the surface, and in their tossings and heavings occasionally came together, crushing and grinding to atoms any object that might be caught between them. They were called the Symplegades, or Clashing Islands. Phineus instructed the Argonauts how to pass this dangerous strait. When they reached the islands they let go a dove, which took her way between the rocks, and passed in safety, only losing some feathers of her tail. Jason and his men seized the favorable moment of the rebound, plied their oars with vigor, and passed safe through, though the islands closed behind them, and actually grazed their stern. They now rowed along the shore till they arrived at the eastern end of the sea, and landed at the kingdom of Colchis.

Jason made known his message to the Colchian king, Æetes, who consented to give up the golden fleece if Jason would yoke to the plow two fire-breathing bulls with brazen feet, and sow the teeth of the dragon that Cadmus had slain, from which it was well known that a crop of armed men would spring up, who would turn their weapons against their producer. Jason accepted the conditions, and a time was set for making the experiment. Previously, however, he found means to plead his cause to Medea, daughter of the King. He promised her marriage, and as they stood before the altar of Hecate he called the goddess to witness his oath. Medea yielded, and by her aid, for she was a potent sorceress, he was furnished with a charm by which he could encounter safely the breath of the fire-breathing bulls and the weapons of the armed men.

At the time appointed, the people assembled at the grove of Mars, and the King assumed his royal seat, while the multitude covered the hillsides. The brazen-footed bulls rushed in, breathing fire that burned up the herbage as they passed. The sound was like the roar of a furnace, and the smoke like that of water upon quicklime. Jason advanced boldly to meet them. He soothed their rage with his voice, patted their necks with fearless hand, and adroitly slipped over them the yoke, and compelled them to drag the plow. The Colchians were amazed; the Greeks shouted for joy. Jason next proceeded to sow the dragon's teeth and plow them in. And soon the crop of armed men sprang up, and no sooner had they reached the surface than they began to brandish their weapons and rush upon Jason. Jason for a time kept his assailants at bay with his sword and shield, till, finding their numbers overwhelming, he resorted to the charm that Medea had taught him, seized a stone and threw it in the midst of his foes. They immediately turned their arms against one another, and soon not one of the dragon's brood was left alive.

It remained to lull to sleep the dragon that guarded the fleece, and this was done by scattering over him a few drops of a preparation that Medea had supplied. At the smell he relaxed his rage, stood for a moment motionless, then shut those great round eyes, that never had been known to shut before, and turned over on his side, fast asleep. Jason seized the fleece, and, with his friends and Medea accompanying, hastened to their vessel, before Æetes, the King, could arrest their departure, and made the best of their way back to Thessaly. Jason delivered the fleece to Pelias, and dedicated the Argo to Neptune.

Halcyone. Ceyx was King of Thessaly, where he reigned in peace, without violence or wrong. He was son of Hesperus, the Day-star, and the glow of his beauty reminded one of his father. Halcyone, the daughter of Æolus, was his wife, and was devotedly attached to him. Ceyx was in deep affliction for the loss of his brother, and direful prodigies following his brother's death made him feel as if the gods were hostile to him. He thought best, therefore, to make a voyage to Claros in Ionia, to consult the oracle of Apollo. But as soon as he disclosed his intention to his wife Halcyone, a shudder ran through her frame, and her face grew deadly pale. "What fault of mine, dearest husband, has turned your affection from me? Where is that love of me that used to be uppermost in your thoughts? Have you learned to feel easy in the absence of Halcyone? Would you rather have me away?" She also endeavored to discourage him, by describing the violence of the winds, which she had known familiarly when she lived at home in her father's house, Æolus being the god of the winds. "They rush together," said she, "with such fury that fire flashes from the conflict. But if you must go," she added, "dear husband, let me go with you; otherwise I shall suffer not only the real evils that you must encounter, but those also that my fears suggest."

He consoled her as well as he could, and finished with these words: "I promise, by the rays of my father, the Day-star, that if fate permits I will return before the moon shall have twice rounded her orb." Then he ordered the vessel to be drawn out of the shiphouse, and the oars and sails to be put aboard. When Halcyone saw these preparations she shuddered, is if with a presentiment of evil. With tears and sobs she said farewell, and then fell senseless to the ground.

The young men pulled vigorously through the waves, with long and measured strokes. Halcyone raised her streaming eyes, and saw her husband standing on the deck, waving his hand to her. She answered his signal till the vessel had receded so far that she could no longer distinguish his form from the rest.

Meanwhile they glided out of the harbor. The seamen drew in their oars and hoisted their sails. When half of their course was passed, as night drew on, the sea began to whiten with swelling waves, and the east wind to blow a gale. The master gave the word to take in sail, but the storm forbade obedience, for such is the roar of the winds and waves his orders were unheard. The men, of their own accord, busied themselves to secure the oars, to strengthen the ship, to reef the sail. The swelling sea seemed lifted up to the heavens, to scatter its foam among the clouds; then sinking away to the bottom assumed the color of the shoal.

Rain fell in torrents, and when the lightning ceased for a moment, the night seemed to add its own darkness to that of the storm. Ceyx thought of Halcyone. No name but hers was on his lips, and while he yearned for her, he yet rejoiced in her absence. Presently the mast was shattered by lightning, the rudder broken, and the triumphant surge curling over looked down upon the wreck. Ceyx held fast to a plank, calling upon his father and his father-in-law for help. But oftenest on his lips was the name of Halcyone. At last the waters overwhelmed him and he sank.

Halcyone, ignorant of all these horrors, counted the days till her husband's promised return. Now she made ready the garments which he should put on, and now what she should wear when he arrived. To all the gods she offered frequent incense, but more than all to Juno. For her husband, who was no more, she prayed incessantly. The goddess, at last, could not bear any longer to be pleaded with for one already dead. So, calling Iris, she said: "Iris, my faithful messenger, go to the drowsy dwelling of Somnus, and tell him to send a vision to Halcyone, in the form of Ceyx, to make known to her the event."

Iris put on her robe of many colors, and tinging the sky with her bow, sought the palace of the King of Sleep. Near the Cimmerian country, a mountain cave is the abode of the dull god Somnus.

Here Phœbus dares not come, either rising, at midday, or setting. Clouds and shadows are exhaled from the ground, and the light glimmers faintly. The bird of dawning, with crested head, never there calls aloud to Aurora, nor watchful dog nor more sagacious goose disturbs the silence. No wild beast, nor cattle, nor branch moves with the wind, nor sound of human conversation breaks the stillness. Silence reigns there; but from the bottom of the rock the River Lethe flows, and by its murmur invites to sleep. Poppies grow abundantly before the door of the cave, and other herbs, from whose juices Night collects slumbers, which she scatters over the darkened earth. There is no gate to the mansion, to creak on its hinges, nor any watchman; but in the midst a couch of black ebony, adorned with black plumes and black curtains. There the god reclines, his limbs relaxed with sleep. Around him lie dreams, resembling all various forms, as many as the harvest bears stalks, or the forest leaves, or the seashore sand grains.

As soon as the goddess entered and brushed away the dreams that hovered around her, her brightness lighted up all the cave. The god, hardly opening his eyes, and ever and anon dropping his beard upon his breast, at last shook himself free from himself, and leaning on his arm, inquired her errand—for he knew who she was. She answered: "Somnus, gentlest of the gods, tranquillizer of minds and soother of care-worn hearts, Juno sends you her commands that you despatch a dream to Halcyone, in the city of Trachine, which shall vividly represent her lost husband and all the events of the wreck."

Having delivered her message, Iris hastened away, for she could not longer endure the stagnant air, and as she felt drowsiness creeping over her, she made her escape, and returned by her bow, the way she came.

Then Somnus called one of his numerous sons, Morpheus, the most expert in counterfeiting forms, and in imitating the walk, the countenance, and mode of speaking, even the clothes and attitudes most characteristic of each. But he only imitates men, leaving it to another to personate birds, beasts, and serpents. Him they call Icelos; and Phantasos is a third, who turns himself into rocks, waters, woods, and other things without life. These wait upon kings and great personages in their sleeping hours, while others move among the common people. Somnus chose, from all the brothers, Morpheus, to perform the command of Iris; then laid his head on his pillow and yielded himself again to repose.

Morpheus flew, making no noise with his wings, and soon came to the Hæmonian city, where, laying aside his wings, he assumed the form of Ceyx. Under that form, but pale like a dead man, naked, he stood before the couch of the wretched wife. His beard seemed soaked with water, and water trickled from his drowned locks. Leaning over the bed, tears streaming from his eyes, he said: "Do you recognize your Ceyx, unhappy wife, or has death too much changed my visage? Behold me, know me, your husband's shade, instead of himself. Your prayers, Halcyone, availed me nothing. I am dead. No more deceive yourself with vain hopes of my return. The stormy winds sank my ship in the Ægean Sea, waves filled my mouth while it called aloud on you. No uncertain messenger tells you this, no vague rumor brings it to your ears. I come in person, a shipwrecked man, to tell you my fate. Arise! give me tears, give me lamentations, let me not go down to Tartarus unwept." To these words Morpheus added the voice that seemed to be that of her husband; he seemed to pour forth genuine tears; his hands had the gestures of Ceyx.

Halcyone, weeping, groaned, and stretched out her arms in her sleep, striving to embrace his body, but grasping only the air. "Stay!" she cried; "whither do you fly? Let us go together." Her own voice awakened her. Starting up, she gazed eagerly around, to see whether he was still present, for the servants, alarmed by her cries, had brought a light. When she found him not, she smote her breast and rent her garments. She cared not to unbind her hair, but tore it wildly. Her nurse asked what was the cause of her grief. "Halcyone is no more," she answered; "she perished with her Ceyx. Utter not words of comfort; he is shipwrecked and dead. I have seen him, I have recognized him. I stretched out my hands to seize him and detain him. His shade vanished, but it was the true shade of my husband. Not with the accustomed features, not with the beauty that was his, but pale, naked, and with his hair wet with sea-water, he appeared to wretched me. Here, in this very spot, the sad vision stood"—and she looked to find the mark of his footsteps. "This it was, this that my presaging mind foreboded, when I implored him not to leave me, to trust himself to the waves. Oh, how I wish, since thou wouldst go, thou hadst taken me with thee! Then I should

"Look! look! comrade, yonder are the cranes of Ibycus!" And suddenly appeared sailing across the sky a dark object which a moment's inspection showed to be a flock of cranes flying directly over the theater. "Of Ibycus! did he say?" The beloved name revived the sorrow in every breast. As wave follows wave over the face of the sea, so ran from mouth to mouth the words: "Of Ibycus! him whom we all lament, whom some murderer's hand laid low! What have the cranes to do with him?" And louder grew the swell of voices, while like a lightning's flash the thought sped through every heart: "Observe the power of the Eumenides! The pious poet shall be avenged! the murderer has informed against himself. Seize the man who uttered that cry, and the other to whom he spoke!"

The faces of the murderers, pale with terror, betrayed their guilt. The people took them before the judge and they confessed their crime and suffered the punishment they deserved.

Io. Juno one day saw that it suddenly grew dark, and suspected that her husband had raised a cloud to hide some of his doings. She brushed away the cloud, and saw her husband on the banks of a glassy river, with a beautiful heifer standing near him. Juno suspected that the heifer's form concealed some fair nymph of mortal mold—as was, indeed, the case; for it was Io, daughter of the river-god Inachus, with whom Jupiter had been flirting, and, when he became aware of the approach of his wife, had changed into that form.

Juno joined her husband, noticed the heifer, praised its beauty, and asked whose it was, and of what herd. Jupiter, to stop questions, replied that it was a fresh creation from the earth. Juno asked to have it as a gift. As he could not refuse without exciting suspicion, he consented. The goddess was not yet relieved of her suspicion; so she delivered the heifer to Argus, to be strictly watched.

Argus had a hundred eyes, and never went to sleep with more than two at a time, so that he kept watch of Io constantly. He suffered her to feed through the day, and at night tied her up with a vile rope round her neck. She would have stretched out her arms to implore freedom of Argus, but she had no arms to stretch out, and her voice was a bellow that frightened even herself. She saw her father and her sisters, went near them, and suffered them to pat her back, and heard them admire her beauty. Her father reached her a tuft of grass, and she licked the outstretched hand. At last she bethought herself of writing, and inscribed her name—it was short—with her hoof on the sand. Inachus recognized it, and, discovering that his daughter was hidden under this disguise, mourned over her, and, embracing her white neck, exclaimed: "Alas! my daughter, it would have been a less grief to lose you altogether!" Argus came and drove her away, and took his seat on a high bank.

Jupiter, calling Mercury, told him to go and despatch Argus. Mercury put on his winged slippers and his cap, took his sleep-producing wand, and leaped down to the earth. There he laid aside his wings, and kept only his wand, as a shepherd driving his flock. As he strolled on he blew upon his pipes. These were what are called the Syrinx or Pandean pipes. Argus listened with delight. "Young man," said he, "come and take a seat by me. There is no better place for your flock to graze in than hereabout." Mercury sat down, talked, and told stories till it grew late, and played upon his pipes his most soothing strains, hoping to lull the watchful eyes to sleep; but all was in vain, for the wary Argus still contrived to keep some of his eyes open.

Among other stories, Mercury told him how the instrument on which he played was invented. "There was a certain nymph, whose name was Syrinx, who was much beloved by the satyrs and spirits of the wood; but she would have none of them, but was a faithful worshiper of Diana, and followed the chase. You would have thought it was Diana herself, had you seen her in her hunting-dress, only that her bow was of horn and Diana's of silver. One day Pan met her, told her just this, and added more of the same sort. She ran away, without stopping to hear his compliments, and he pursued till she came to the bank of the river, where he overtook her, and she had only time to call for help on her friends the water-nymphs. Pan threw his arms around what he supposed to be the form of the nymph, and found he embraced only a tuft of reeds. As he breathed a sigh, the air sounded through the reeds and produced a plaintive melody. The god, charmed with the novelty, and with the sweetness of the music, said, 'Thus, then, at least, you shall be mine.' And he took some of the reeds, and placing them together, of unequal lengths, side by side, made an instrument which he called Syrinx, in honor of the nymph." Before Mercury had finished his story Argus's eyes were all asleep. As his head nodded forward on his breast, Mercury with one stroke cut his neck through, and tumbled his head down the rocks. Juno took the hundred eyes and put them as ornaments on the tail of her peacock, where they remain to this day.

She then sent a gadfly to torment Io, who fled over the whole world from its pursuit. She swam through the Ionian Sea, which derived its name from her, then roamed over the plains of Illyria, ascended Mount Hæmus, and crossed the Thracian strait, thence named the Bosporus (cow-ford), rambled on through Scythia and the country of the Cimmerians, and arrived on the banks of the Nile. At last Jupiter interceded for her, and upon his promising not to pay her any more attentions Juno consented to restore her to her form.

Latona and the **Rustics.** Some countrymen of Lycia once insulted the goddess Latona, but not with impunity. Royal Juno, in jealousy, drove her from land to land, denying her any spot of earth whereon to rear her twins. Bearing in her arms the infant deities, Latona reached Lycia, weary with her burden and parched with thirst. By chance she espied in the valley a pond of clear water, where the country people were at work gathering willows and osiers. The goddess approached, and kneeling on the bank would have slaked her thirst in the cool stream, but the rustics forbade her. "Why do you refuse me water?" said she; "water is free to all. Nature allows no one to claim as property the sunshine, the air, or the water. I come to take my share of the common blessing. Yet I ask it of you as a favor. I have no intention of washing my limbs in it, weary though they be, but only to quench my thirst. My mouth is so dry that I can hardly speak. A draught of water would be nectar to me; it would revive me, and I would own myself indebted to you for life itself. Let these infants move your pity, who stretch out their little arms as if to plead for me"; and the children, as it happened, were stretching out their arms.

But the clowns persisted in their rudeness; they even added jeers and threats of violence if she did not leave the place. Nor was this all. They waded into the pond and stirred up the mud with their feet, so as to make the water unfit to drink. Latona was so angry that she ceased to mind her thirst. She no longer supplicated the clowns, but lifting her hands to heaven exclaimed, "May they never quit that pool, but pass their lives there!" And it came to pass accordingly. They now live in the water, sometimes totally submerged, then raising their heads above the surface or swimming upon it.

Sometimes they come out upon the bank, but soon leap back again into the water. They still use their bass voices in railing, and though they have the water all to themselves, are not ashamed to croak in the midst of it. Their voices are harsh, their throats bloated, their mouths have become stretched by constant railing, their necks have shrunk up and disappeared, and their heads are joined to their bodies. Their backs are green, their disproportioned bellies white; and in short they are now frogs, and dwell in the slimy pool.

Leucothea and Palæmon. Ino, the daughter of Cadmus and wife of Athamas, flying from her frantic husband with her little son Melicertes in her arms, sprang from a cliff into the sea. The gods, out of compassion, made her a goddess of the sea, under the name of Leucothea, and him a god under that of Palæmon. Both were held powerful to save from shipwreck and were invoked by sailors. Palæmon was usually represented riding on a dolphin. The Isthmian games were celebrated in his honor. He was called Portunus by the Romans, and believed to have jurisdiction of the ports and shores.

Linus. Linus was the instructor of Hercules in music, but having one day reproved his pupil rather harshly, he roused the anger of Hercules, who struck him with his lyre and killed him.

Marsyas. Minerva invented the flute, and played upon it to the delight of all the celestial auditors; but the mischievous urchin Cupid having dared to laugh at the queer face the goddess made while playing, Minerva threw the instrument away, and it fell to earth, and was found by Marsyas. He blew upon it, and drew from it such ravishing sounds that he was tempted to challenge Apollo himself to a musical contest. The god of course triumphed, and punished Marsyas by flaying him alive.

Medusa. The Grææ were three sisters who were gray-haired from their birth, whence their name. The Gorgons were monstrous females with huge teeth like those of swine, brazen claws, and snaky hair. None of these beings make much figure in mythology except Medusa, the Gorgon. We mention them chiefly to introduce an ingenious theory of some modern writers, namely, that the Gorgons and Grææ were only personifications of the terrors of the sea, the former denoting the *strong* billows of the wide open main, and the latter the *white*-crested waves that dash against the rocks of the coast. Their names in Greek signify the above epithets.

Perseus was the son of Jupiter and Danaë. His grandfather

She too, when she shall have filled her term of life, will rightly be yours. But till then, grant her to me, I beseech you. If you deny me, I cannot return alone; you shall triumph in the death of us both."

As he sang these tender strains, the very ghosts shed tears. Tantalus, in spite of his thirst, stopped for a moment his efforts for water, Ixion's wheel stood still, the vulture ceased to tear the giant's liver, the daughters of Danaüs rested from their task of drawing water in a sieve, and Sisyphus sat on his rock to listen. Then for the first time, it is said, the cheeks of the Furies were wet with tears. Proserpine could not resist, and Pluto himself gave way. Eurydice was called. She came from among the new-arrived ghosts, limping with her wounded foot. Orpheus was permitted to take her away with him on one condition, that he should not turn round to look at her till they should have reached the upper air. Under this condition they proceeded, he leading, she following, through passages dark and steep, in total silence, till they had nearly reached the outlet into the cheerful upper world, when Orpheus, in a moment of forgetfulness, to assure himself that she was still following, cast a glance behind him, when instantly she was borne away. Stretching out their arms to embrace each other, they grasped only the air. "Farewell," she said, "a last farewell," and was hurried away, so fast that the sound hardly reached his ears.

Orpheus endeavored to follow her, and besought permission to return and try once more for her release; but the stern ferryman refused passage. Seven days he lingered about, without food or sleep; then bitterly accusing of cruelty the powers of Erebus, he sang his complaints to the rocks and mountains, melting the hearts of tigers and moving the oaks from their stations. He held himself aloof from womankind, dwelling constantly on the recollection of his sad mischance. The Thracian maidens tried their best to captivate him, but he repelled their advances. They bore with him as long as they could; but finding him insensible one day, excited by the rites of Bacchus, one of them exclaimed, "See yonder our despiser!" and threw her javelin at him. The weapon, as soon as it came within the sound of his lyre, fell harmless at his feet. So also did the stones they threw at him. But the women raised a scream and drowned the voice of the music, and then the missiles reached him and soon were stained with his blood. The maniacs tore him limb from limb, and threw his head and his lyre into the river Hebrus, down which they floated, murmuring sad music, to which the shores responded with a plaintive symphony. The Muses gathered up the fragments of his body and buried them at Libethra, where the nightingale is said to sing over his grave more sweetly than in any other part of Greece. His lyre was placed by Jupiter among the stars. His shade passed a second time to Tartarus, where he sought out his Eurydice and eagerly embraced her. They roam the happy fields together now, sometimes he leading, sometimes she.

Pegasus and the **Chimæra.** When Perseus cut off Medusa's head, the blood sinking into the earth produced the winged horse Pegasus. Minerva caught and tamed him, and presented him to the Muses. The fountain Hippocrene, on the Muses' mountain Helicon, was opened by a kick from his hoof.

The Chimæra was a fearful monster, breathing fire. The fore part of its body was a compound of the lion and the goat, and the hind part a dragon's. It made great havoc in Lycia, so that the King Iobates sought for a hero to destroy it. At that time a gallant young warrior, whose name was Bellerophon, arrived at his court. He brought letters from Prœtus, the son-in-law of Iobates, recommending Bellerophon in the warmest terms as an unconquerable hero, but adding at the close a request to his father-in-law to put him to death. Prœtus was jealous of him, suspecting that his wife Antea looked with too much admiration on the young warrior.

Iobates was puzzled what to do, not willing to violate the claims of hospitality, yet wishing to oblige his son-in-law. A lucky thought occurred to him, to send Bellerophon to combat with the Chimæra. Bellerophon accepted the proposal, but before proceeding to the combat, consulted the soothsayer Polyidus, who advised him to procure the horse Pegasus for the conflict. For this purpose he directed him to pass the night in the temple of Minerva. He did so, and as he slept Minerva came to him and gave him a golden bridle. When he awoke the bridle remained in his hand. Minerva also showed him Pegasus drinking at the well of Pirene, and at sight of the bridle the winged steed willingly suffered himself to be taken. Bellerophon mounted him, rose with him into the air, soon found the Chimæra, and gained an easy victory.

After the conquest of the Chimæra, Bellerophon was exposed to further trials and labors by his unfriendly host, but by the aid of

Pegasus he triumphed in them all; till at last Iobates, seeing that the hero was a special favorite of the gods, gave him his daughter in marriage and made him his successor on the throne. At last Bellerophon by his pride and presumption drew upon himself the anger of the gods; it is said he even attempted to fly up into heaven on his winged steed; but Jupiter sent a gadfly, which stung Pegasus and made him throw his rider, who became lame and blind in consequence. After this Bellerophon wandered lonely through the Aleian field, avoiding the paths of men, and died miserably.

Perseus and **Atlas.** After the slaughter of Medusa, Perseus, bearing with him the head of the Gorgon, flew far and wide, over land and sea. As night came on, he reached the western limit of the earth, where the sun goes down, the realm of King Atlas, whose bulk surpassed that of all other men. He was rich in flocks and herds and had no neighbor or rival. But his chief pride was in his gardens, whose fruit was of gold, hanging from golden branches, half hidden with golden leaves. Perseus said to him: "I come as a guest. If you honor illustrious descent, I claim Jupiter for my father; if mighty deeds, I plead the conquest of the Gorgon. I seek rest and food." But Atlas remembered that an ancient prophecy had warned him that a son of Jove should one day rob him of his golden apples. So he answered, "Begone! for neither your false claims of glory nor parentage shall protect you"; and he attempted to thrust him out. Perseus, finding the giant too strong for him, said, "Since you value my friendship so little, deign to accept a present"; and turning his face away, he held up the Gorgon's head. Atlas, with all his bulk, was changed into stone. His beard and hair became forests, his arms and shoulders cliffs, his head a summit, and his bones rocks. Each part increased in bulk till he became a mountain, and (such was the pleasure of the gods) heaven with all its stars rests upon his shoulders.

Penelope. Penelope was the daughter of Icarius, a Spartan prince. Ulysses, King of Ithaca, sought her in marriage, and won her. When the moment came for the bride to leave her father's house, Icarius, unable to bear the thought of parting with his daughter, tried to persuade her to remain with him, and not accompany her husband to Ithaca. Ulysses gave Penelope her choice, to stay or to go with him. Penelope made no reply, but dropped her veil over her face. Icarius urged her no further, but when she was gone he erected a statue to Modesty on the spot where they had parted.

Ulysses and Penelope had not enjoyed their union more than a year when it was interrupted by the events that called Ulysses to the Trojan war.   During his long absence, and when it was doubtful whether he still lived, and highly improbable that he would ever return, Penelope was importuned by numerous suitors, from whom there seemed no refuge but in choosing one of them for her husband. Penelope, however, employed every art to gain time, still hoping for Ulysses's return.   One of her arts of delay was engaging in the preparation of a robe for the funeral canopy of Laertes, her husband's father.   She pledged herself to make her choice among the suitors when the robe was finished.   During the day she worked at the robe, but in the night she undid the work of the day.   This is the famous Penelope's web, which is used as a proverbial expression for anything that is perpetually doing but never done.

Phaëton. Phaëton was the son of Phœbus Apollo and the nymph Clymene.   One day a schoolfellow laughed at the idea of his being the son of the god, and Phaëton went in rage and shame and reported it to his mother.   "If," said he, "I am indeed of heavenly birth, give me, mother, some proof of it, and establish my claim to the honor."   Clymene stretched forth her hands toward the skies, and said: "I call to witness the Sun which looks down upon us, that I have told you the truth.   If I speak falsely, let this be the last time I behold his light.   But it needs not much labor to go and inquire for yourself; the land whence the Sun rises lies next to ours.   Go and demand of him whether he will own you as a son."   Phaëton heard with delight.   He traveled to India, which lies directly in the regions of sunrise, and, full of hope and pride, approached the goal whence his parent begins his course.

The palace of the Sun stood reared aloft on columns, glittering with gold and precious stones, while polished ivory formed the ceilings, and silver the doors.   The workmanship surpassed the material; for upon the walls Vulcan had represented earth, sea, and skies, with their inhabitants.   In the sea were the nymphs, some sporting in the waves, some riding on the backs of fishes, while others sat upon the rocks and dried their sea-green hair.   Their faces were not all alike, nor yet unlike—but such as sisters' ought to be.   The earth had its towns and forests and rivers and rustic divinities. Over all was carved the likeness of the glorious heaven; and on the silver doors the twelve signs of the zodiac, six on each side.

Clymene's son advanced up the steep ascent, and entered the halls of his disputed father. Phœbus, arrayed in a purple vesture, sat on a throne that glittered as with diamonds. On his right hand and his left stood the Day, the Month, and the Year, and, at regular intervals, the Hours. Spring stood with her head crowned with flowers, and Summer, with garment cast aside, and a garland formed of spears of ripened grain, and Autumn, with his feet stained with grape-juice, and icy Winter, with his hair stiffened with hoar frost. Surrounded by these attendants, the Sun, with the eye that sees everything, beheld the youth dazzled with the novelty and splendor of the scene, and inquired the purpose of his errand. The youth replied: "Oh, light of the boundless world, Phœbus, my father—if you permit me to use that name—give me some proof, I beseech you, by which I may be known as yours." He ceased; and his father, laying aside the beams that shone all around his head, bade him approach, and embracing him, said: "My son, you deserve not to be disowned, and I confirm what your mother has told you. To put an end to your doubts, ask what you will, the gift shall be yours. I call to witness that dreadful lake, which I never saw, but which we gods swear by in our most solemn engagements." Phaëton immediately asked to be permitted for one day to drive the chariot of the sun. The father repented of his promise; thrice and four times he shook his radiant head in warning. "I have spoken rashly," said he; "this only request I would fain deny. I beg you to withdraw it. It is not a safe boon, nor one, my Phaëton, suited to your youth and strength. Your lot is mortal, and you ask what is beyond a mortal's power. In your ignorance you aspire to do that which not even the gods themselves may do. None but I may drive the flaming car of day. Not even Jupiter, whose terrible right arm hurls the thunderbolts. The first part of the way is steep, and such as the horses when fresh in the morning can hardly climb; the middle is high in the heavens, whence I myself can scarcely, without alarm, look down and behold the earth and sea stretched beneath me. The last part of the road descends rapidly, and requires most careful driving. Tethys, who is waiting to receive me, often trembles for me lest I should fall headlong. Add to all this, the heaven is all the time turning round and carrying the

stars with it. I have to be perpetually on my guard lest that movement, which sweeps everything else along, should hurry me also
away. Suppose I should lend you the chariot, what would you do?
Could you keep your course while the sphere was revolving under
you? Perhaps you think there are forests and cities, the abodes of
gods, and palaces and temples on the way. On the contrary, the
road is through the midst of frightful monsters. You pass by the
horns of the Bull, in front of the Archer, and near the Lion's jaws,
and where the Scorpion stretches its arms in one direction and the
Crab in another. Nor will you find it easy to guide those horses, with
their breasts full of fire that they breathe forth from their mouths and
nostrils. I can hardly govern them myself, when they are unruly
and resist the reins. Beware, my son, lest I be the donor of a fatal
gift; recall your request while yet you may. Do you ask me for a
proof that you are sprung from my blood? I give you a proof in my
fears for you."

But the youth rejected all admonition, and held to his demand.
So, having resisted as long as he could, Phœbus at last led the way to
the lofty chariot.

It was of gold, the gift of Vulcan; the axle was of gold, the pole
and wheels of gold, the spokes of silver. Along the seat were rows
of chrysolites and diamonds, which reflected all around the brightness
of the sun. While the daring youth gazed in admiration, the early
Dawn threw open the purple doors of the east, and showed the path-
way strewn with roses. The stars withdrew, marshaled by the Day-
star, which last of all retired also. The father, when he saw the earth
beginning to glow, and the Moon preparing to retire, ordered the
Hours to harness up the horses. They obeyed, and led forth from
the lofty stalls the steeds full fed with ambrosia, and attached the
reins. Then the father bathed the face of his son with a powerful
unguent, and made him capable of enduring the brightness of the
flame. He set the rays on his head, and, with a foreboding sigh, said:
"If, my son, you will in this at least heed my advice, spare the whip
and hold tight the reins. They go fast enough of their own accord;
the labor is to hold them in. You are not to take the straight road
directly between the five circles, but turn off to the left. Keep within
the limit of the middle zone, and avoid the northern and the southern
alike. You will see the marks of the wheels, and they will serve to
guide you. And, that the skies and the earth may each receive their

due share of heat, go not too high, or you will burn the heavenly dwellings, nor too low, or you will set the earth on fire; the middle course is safest and best." The agile youth sprang into the chariot, stood erect, and grasped the reins with delight, pouring out thanks to his reluctant parent.

The horses dart forward, cleave the opposing clouds, and outrun the morning breezes. The steeds soon perceived that the load they drew was lighter than usual; and as a ship without ballast is tossed hither and thither on the sea, so the chariot, without its accustomed weight, was dashed about as if empty. They rushed headlong and left the traveled road. Phaëton was alarmed, and knew not how to guide them; nor, if he knew, had he the power. Then the Great and Little Bear were scorched with heat, and the Serpent which lies coiled up round the north pole, torpid and harmless, grew warm, and with warmth felt its rage revive. Boötes, they say, fled away, though encumbered with his plow.

Phaëton saw with terror the monstrous forms scattered over the surface of heaven. Here the Scorpion extended his two great arms, with his tail and crooked claws stretching over two signs of the zodiac. When the boy beheld him, reeking with poison and menacing with his fangs, his courage failed, and the reins fell from his hands. The horses, when they felt them loose on their backs, dashed headlong, and unrestrained went off into unknown regions of the sky, in among the stars, hurling the chariot over pathless places, now in high heaven, now down almost to the earth. The clouds begin to smoke, and the mountaintops take fire; the fields are parched with heat, the plants wither, the trees with their leafy branches burn, the harvest is ablaze. Great cities perished, with their walls and towers; whole nations with their people were consumed to ashes. The forest-clad mountains burned. Her cold climate was no protection to Scythia; Caucasus burned, and Ossa and Pindus, and, greater than both, Olympus; the Alps high in air, and the Apennines crowned with clouds. Then, it is believed, the people of Æthiopia became black by the blood being forced so suddenly to the surface, and the Libyan desert was dried up to the condition in which it remains to this day. Nile fled away and hid his head in the desert, and there it still remains concealed. Where he used to discharge his waters through seven mouths into the sea, there seven dry channels alone remained. The earth cracked open, and through the chinks light broke into Tartarus, and frightened the king of shadows and his queen. The sea shrank up. Thrice Neptune essayed to raise his head above the surface, and thrice was driven back by the heat. Earth, surrounded as she was by waters, yet with head and shoulders bare, looked up to heaven, and with a husky voice called on Jupiter. "O ruler of the gods, if I have deserved this treatment, and it is your will that I perish with fire, why withhold your thunderbolts? Let me at least fall by your hand."

Then Jupiter omnipotent, calling to witness all the gods, including him who had lent the chariot, and showing them that all was lost unless some speedy remedy were applied, mounted the lofty tower whence he diffuses clouds over the earth, and hurls the forked lightnings. But at that time not a cloud was to be found to interpose for a screen to earth, nor was a shower remaining unexhausted. He thundered, and brandishing a lightning-bolt in his right hand launched it against the charioteer, and struck him at the same moment from his seat and from existence. Phaëton, with his hair on fire, fell headlong, like a shooting star, and Eridanus, the great river, received him and cooled his burning frame. The Italian Naiads reared a tomb for him. His sisters, the Heliades, as they lamented his fate, were turned into poplar-trees, on the banks of the river, and their tears became amber as they dropped into the stream.

Prometheus and **Pandora.** Before earth and sea and heaven were created all things wore one aspect, to which we give the name of Chaos—a confused and shapeless mass; the earth was not solid, the sea was not fluid, and the air was not transparent. God and Nature at last interposed and separated earth from sea, and heaven from both. The fiery part, being the lightest, sprang up and formed the skies; the air was next in weight and place. The earth, being heavier, sank below; and the water took the lowest place, and buoyed up the earth.

The air being cleared, the stars began to appear, fishes took possession of the sea, birds of the air, and four-footed beasts of the land.

Prometheus took some of this earth, and kneading it up with water, made man in the image of the gods. He gave him an upright stature, so that while all other animals turn their faces downward, and look to the earth, man raises his to heaven, and gazes on the stars.

India. Homer tells us that the cranes used to migrate every winter to the Pygmies' country, and their appearance was the signal of bloody warfare to the puny inhabitants, who had to take up arms to defend their cornfields against the rapacious strangers. The Pygmies and their enemies the Cranes form the subject of several works of art.

Later writers tell of an army of Pygmies which, finding Hercules asleep, made preparations to attack him, as if they were about to attack a city. But the hero awaking laughed at the little warriors, wrapped some of them up in his lion's-skin, and carried them to Eurystheus.

Pyramus and **Thisbe.** Pyramus was the handsomest youth, and Thisbe the fairest maiden, in all Babylonia, where Semiramis reigned. Their parents occupied adjoining houses; and neighborhood brought the young people together, and acquaintance ripened into love. They would gladly have married, but their parents forbade. One thing, however, they could not forbid—that love should glow with equal ardor in the bosoms of both. In the wall that parted the two houses there was a crack, caused by some fault in the structure. No one had remarked it before, but the lovers discovered it, and tender messages used to pass backward and forward through the gap. As they stood, Pyramus on this side, Thisbe on that, their breaths would mingle.

"Cruel wall," they said, "why do you keep two lovers apart? But we will not be ungrateful. We owe you, we confess, the privilege of transmitting loving words to willing ears."

Such words they uttered on different sides of the wall; and when night came and they must say farewell, they pressed their lips upon the wall, she on her side, he on his.

One morning, when Aurora had put out the stars, and the sun had melted the frost from the grass, they met at the accustomed spot. Then they agreed that next night they would slip away from watchful eyes, leave their dwellings and walk out into the fields, and repair to a well-known edifice, called the Tomb of Ninus, and that the one who came first should await the other at the foot of a certain tree. It was a white mulberry-tree, and stood near a cool spring. Cautiously Thisbe stole forth, unobserved by the family, her head covered with a veil, made her way to the monument and sat down under the tree. As she sat alone in the dim light of the evening she descried a lioness, her jaws reeking with recent slaughter, approaching the fountain to slake her thirst. Thisbe fled at the sight, and sought refuge in the hollow of a rock. As she fled she dropped her veil. The lioness, after drinking at the spring, turned to retreat to the woods, and seeing the veil on the ground, tossed and rent it with her bloody mouth.

Pyramus, having been delayed, now approached the place of meeting. He saw in the sand the footsteps of the lion, and the color fled from his cheeks at the sight. Presently he found the veil all rent and bloody.

"O hapless girl," said he, "I have been the cause of thy death! Thou, more worthy of life than I, hast fallen the first victim. I will follow. I am the guilty cause, in tempting thee forth to a place of such peril, and not being myself on the spot to guard thee. Come forth, ye lions, from the rocks, and tear this guilty body with your teeth."

He took up the veil, carried it with him to the appointed tree, and covered it with kisses and with tears.

"*My* blood also shall stain your texture," said he, and drawing his sword plunged it into his heart.

The blood spurted from the wound, and tinged the white mulberries of the tree all red; and sinking into the earth reached the roots, so that the red color mounted through the trunk to the fruit.

By this time Thisbe, still trembling with fear, yet wishing not to disappoint her lover, stepped cautiously forth. When she came to the spot and saw the changed color of the mulberries she doubted whether it was the same place. While she hesitated she saw the form of one struggling in the agonies of death. As soon as she recognized her lover, she screamed and beat her breast; embracing the lifeless body, pouring tears into its wounds, and imprinting kisses on the cold lips.

"O Pyramus," she cried, "what has done this? Answer me, Pyramus; it is your own Thisbe that speaks. Hear me, dearest, and lift that drooping head!"

At the name of Thisbe Pyramus opened his eyes, then closed them again. She saw her veil stained with blood and the scabbard empty of its sword.

"Thy own hand has slain thee, and for my sake," she said. "I too can be brave for once, and my love is as strong as thine. I will follow thee in death, for I have been the cause; and death, which alone could part us, shall not prevent my joining thee. And ye, unhappy parents of us both, deny us not our united request. As love and death have joined us, let one tomb contain us. And thou, tree, retain the marks of slaughter. Let thy berries still serve for memorials of our blood."

So saying she plunged the sword into her breast. The two bodies were buried in one sepulcher, and the tree ever afterward brought forth purple berries, as it does to this day.

Rhœcus. The Hamadryads could appreciate services as well as punish injuries. Rhœcus, happening to see an oak just ready to fall, ordered his servants to prop it up. The nymph, who had been on the point of perishing with the tree, came and expressed her gratitude to him for saving her life, and bade him ask what reward he would. Rhœcus boldly asked her love, and the nymph yielded to his desire. She at the same time charged him to be constant, and told him that a bee should be her messenger, and let him know when she would admit his society. One time the bee came to Rhœcus when he was playing at draughts, and he carelessly brushed it away. This so incensed the nymph that she deprived him of sight.

Rural Deities. Pan, the god of woods and fields, of flocks and shepherds, dwelt in grottos, wandered on the mountains and in valleys, and amused himself with the chase or in leading the dances of the nymphs. He was fond of music, and, as we have seen, was the inventor of the syrinx, or shepherd's pipe, which he himself played in a masterly manner. Pan, like other gods who dwelt in forests, was dreaded by those whose occupations caused them to pass through the woods by night, for the gloom and loneliness of such scenes dispose the mind to superstitious fears. Hence sudden fright without any visible cause was ascribed to Pan, and was called Panic terror. As the name of the god signifies *all*, Pan came to be considered a symbol of the universe and personification of Nature; and later still to be regarded as a representative of all the gods and of heathenism itself.

Sylvanus and Faunus were Latin divinities, whose characteristics are so nearly the same as those of Pan that we may safely consider them as the same personage under different names.

The wood-nymphs, Pan's partners in the dance, were but one class of nymphs. There were besides them the Naiads, who presided over brooks and fountains, the Oreads, nymphs of mountains and grottos, and the Nereids, sea-nymphs. The three last named were immortal, but the wood-nymphs, called Dryads or Hamadryads, were believed to perish with the trees that had been their abode, and with which they had come into existence. It was therefore an impious act wantonly to destroy a tree, and in some aggravated cases was severely punished, as in the instance of Erisichthon.

It was a pleasing trait in the old Paganism that it loved to trace in every operation of nature the agency of deity. The imagination of the Greeks peopled all the regions of earth and sea with divinities, to whose agency it attributed those phenomena which our philosophy ascribes to the operation of the laws of nature.

According to an early Christian tradition, when the heavenly host told the shepherds at Bethlehem of the birth of Christ, a deep groan, heard through all the isles of Greece, told that the great Pan was dead, and that all the royalty of Olympus was dethroned, and the several deities were sent wandering in cold and darkness.

Thamyris. This was an ancient Thracian bard, who in his presumption challenged the Muses to a trial of skill, and being overcome in the contest, was deprived by them of his sight.

Theseus. Theseus was the son of Ægeus, King of Athens, and of Æthra, daughter of the King of Trœzen. He was brought up at Trœzen, and when arrived at manhood, was to go to Athens and present himself to his father. Ægeus, on parting from Æthra, before the birth of his son, placed his sword and shoes under a large stone, and directed her to send his son to him when he became strong enough to roll away the stone and take them from under it. When she thought the time had come, his mother led Theseus to the stone, and he removed it with ease, and took the sword and shoes. As the roads were infested with robbers, his grandfather pressed him earnestly to take the shorter and safer way to his father's country, by sea; but the youth, feeling in himself the spirit and the soul of a hero, and eager to signalize himself like Hercules, with whose fame all Greece then rang, by destroying the evil-doers and monsters that oppressed the country, determined to journey by land.

His first day's journey brought him to Epidaurus, where dwelt a man named Periphetes, a son of Vulcan. This ferocious savage always went armed with a club of iron, and all travelers stood in terror of his violence. When he saw Theseus approach, he assailed him, but he speedily fell beneath the blows of the young hero, who took possession of his club, and bore it ever afterward as a memorial of his first victory.

Several similar contests with petty tyrants and marauders followed, in all of which Theseus was victorious. One of these evil-doers was called Procrustes, or the Stretcher. He had an iron bedstead, on which he used to tie all travelers who fell into his hands. If they were shorter than the bed, he stretched their limbs to make them fit it; if they were longer than the bed, he lopped off a part. Theseus served him as he had served others.

Having overcome all the perils of the road, Theseus at last reached Athens, where new dangers awaited him. Medea, the sorceress, who had fled from Corinth after her separation from Jason, had become the wife of Ægeus, the father of Theseus. Knowing by her arts who he was, and fearing the loss of her influence with her husband, if Theseus should be acknowledged as his son, she filled the mind of Ægeus with suspicions of the young stranger, and induced him to present him a cup of poison; but at the moment when Theseus stepped forward to take it, the sight of the sword he wore discovered to his father who he was and prevented the fatal draught. Medea, detected in her arts, fled from deserved punishment and arrived in Asia, where the country afterward called Media received its name from her. Theseus was acknowledged by his father, and was declared his successor.

The Athenians were at that time in deep affliction, on account of the tribute they were forced to pay to Minos, King of Crete. This tribute consisted of seven youths and seven maidens, who were sent every year to be devoured by the Minotaur, a monster with a bull's body and a human head. It was exceedingly strong and fierce, and was kept in a labyrinth constructed by Dædalus, so artfully contrived that whoever was enclosed in it could by no means find his way out unassisted. Here the Minotaur roamed and was fed with human victims.

Theseus resolved to deliver his countrymen from this calamity or to die in the attempt. Accordingly, when the time of sending off the tribute came, and the youths and maidens were drawn by lot to be sent, he offered himself as one of the victims, in spite of the entreaties of his father. The ship departed under black sails, as usual, which Theseus promised his father to change for white in case of his returning victorious. When they arrived in Crete, the youths and maidens were exhibited before Minos; and Ariadne, daughter of the King, being present, became deeply enamored of Theseus, by whom her love was readily returned. She furnished him with a sword with which to encounter the Minotaur, and with a clew of thread by which he might find his way out of the labyrinth. He slew the Minotaur, escaped from the labyrinth, and, taking Ariadne as his companion, sailed with his rescued companions for Athens. On their way they stopped at the island of Naxos, where Theseus abandoned Ariadne, leaving her asleep. His excuse was that Minerva appeared to him in a dream and commanded him to do so.

On approaching the coast of Attica, Theseus forgot the signal appointed by his father, and neglected to raise the white sails, and the old King, thinking his son had perished, put an end to his own life. Theseus thus became King of Athens.

One of the most celebrated of the adventures of Theseus was his expedition against the Amazons. He assailed them before they had recovered from the attack of Hercules, and carried off their queen, Antiope. The Amazons in their turn invaded the country of Athens and penetrated into the city itself; and the final battle in which Theseus overcame them was fought in the very midst of the city.

The friendship between Theseus and Pirithoüs was most intimate, yet it originated in the midst of arms. Pirithoüs had made an irruption into the plain of Marathon, and carried off the herds of the King of Athens. Theseus went to repel the plunderers. The moment Pirithoüs beheld him, he was seized with admiration; he stretched out his hand as a token of peace, and cried: "Be judge thyself—what satisfaction dost thou require?" "Thy friendship," replied the Athenian, and they swore inviolable fidelity. Their deeds corresponded to their professions, and they ever continued to be true brothers in arms. Each of them aspired to espouse a daughter of Jupiter. Theseus fixed his choice on Helen, then but a child, afterward so celebrated as the cause of the Trojan war, and with the aid of his friend he carried her off. Pirithoüs aspired to the wife of the monarch of Erebus; and Theseus, though aware of the danger, accompanied the ambitious lover in his descent to the under-world. But Pluto seized and set them on an enchanted rock at his palace gate, where they remained till Hercules arrived and liberated Theseus, leaving Pirithoüs to his fate.

After the death of Antiope, Theseus married Phædra, daughter of Minos, King of Crete. Phædra saw in Hippolytus, the son of Theseus, a youth endowed with all the graces and virtues of his father, and of an age corresponding to her own. She loved him, but he repelled her advances, and her love was changed to hate. She used her influence over her infatuated husband to cause him to be jealous of his son, and he called the vengeance of Neptune upon him. As Hippolytus was one day driving his chariot along the shore, a sea-monster raised himself above the waters and frightened the horses so that they ran away and dashed the chariot to pieces. Hippolytus was killed, but by Diana's assistance Æsculapius restored him to life. Diana removed Hippolytus from the power of his father and stepmother, and placed him in Italy under the protection of the nymph Egeria.

Theseus at last lost the favor of his people, and retired to the court of Lycomedes, King of Scyros, who at first received him kindly, but afterward treacherously slew him. In a later age the Athenian general Cimon discovered the place where his remains were laid, and caused them to be removed to Athens, where they were deposited in a temple called the Theseum, erected in honor of the hero.

Theseus is a semi-historical personage. It is recorded of him that he united the several tribes by whom the territory of Attica was then possessed into one state, of which Athens was the capital. In commemoration of this important event, he instituted the festival of Panathenæa, in honor of Minerva, the patron deity of Athens. This festival differed from the other Grecian games chiefly in two particulars. It was peculiar to the Athenians, and its chief feature was a solemn procession in which the peplus or sacred robe of Minerva was carried to the Parthenon, and suspended before the statute of the goddess. The peplus was covered with embroidery, worked by select virgins of the noblest families in Athens. The procession consisted of persons of all ages and both sexes. The old men carried olive branches in their hands, and the young men bore arms. The young women carried baskets on their heads, containing the sacred utensils, cakes, and all things necessary for the sacrifices.

Venus and **Adonis.** Venus, playing one day with her boy Cupid, wounded her bosom with one of his arrows. She pushed him away, but the wound was deeper than she thought. Before it healed she beheld Adonis, and was captivated with him. She no longer took any interest in her favorite resorts—Paphos, and Cnidos, and Amathos, rich in metals. She absented herself even from heaven, for Adonis was dearer to her than heaven. Him she followed and bore him company. She who used to love to recline in the shade, with no care but to cultivate her charms, now rambled through the woods and over the hills, dressed like the huntress Diana. She charged Adonis to beware of dangerous animals. "Be brave toward the timid," said she; "courage against the courageous is not safe. Beware how you expose yourself to danger, and put my happiness to risk. Attack not the beasts that Nature has armed with weapons. I do not value your glory so high as to consent to purchase it by such exposure. Your youth, and the beauty that charms Venus, will not touch the hearts of lions and bristly boars. Think of their terrible claws and prodigious strength! I hate the whole race of them. Do you ask me why?" Then she told him the story of Atalanta and Hippomenes, who were changed into lions for their ingratitude to her.

Having given him this warning, she mounted her chariot drawn by swans, and drove away through the air. But Adonis was too noble to heed such counsels. The dogs had roused a wild boar from his lair, and the youth threw his spear and wounded the animal with a sidelong stroke. The beast drew out the weapon with his jaws, and rushed after Adonis, who turned and ran; but the boar overtook him, and buried his tusks in his side, and stretched him dying upon the plain.

Venus, in her swan-drawn chariot, had not reached Cyprus when she heard the groans of her beloved, and turned her white-winged coursers back to earth. As she drew near and saw his body bathed in blood, she alighted, and bending over it beat her breast and tore her hair. Reproaching the Fates, she said: "Yet theirs shall be but a partial triumph; memorials of my grief shall endure, and the spectacle of your death, my Adonis, and of my lamentation shall be annually renewed. Your blood shall be changed into a flower; that consolation none can envy me." Thus speaking, she sprinkled nectar on the blood; and as they mingled, bubbles rose as in a pool, on which raindrops fall, and in an hour a flower of a bloody hue like that of the pomegranate sprang up. But it is short-lived. It is said

The Birth of Venus

Photogravure on French Plate Paper after a painting by W. Bouguereau, in the Luxembourg Palace, Paris.

The Birth of Venus

Photogravure on French Plate Paper after a painting by
W. Bouguereau, in the Luxembourg
Palace, Paris.

By main force Ulysses dragged these men away, and he was even obliged to tie them under the benches of his ship.

They next arrived at the country of the Cyclopes. The Cyclopes were giants, who inhabited an island of which they were the only possessors. The name means "round eye," and these giants were so called because they had but one eye, and that in the middle of the forehead. They dwelt in caves and fed on the wild productions of the island and on what their flocks yielded, for they were shepherds. Ulysses left the main body of his ships at anchor, and with one vessel went to the Cyclopes' island to explore for supplies. He landed with his companions, carrying with them a jar of wine for a present, and coming to a large cave they entered it, and finding no one within examined its contents. They found it stored with the riches of the flock, quantities of cheese, pails and bowls of milk, lambs and kids in their pens, all in fine order. Presently arrived the master of the cave, Polyphemus, bearing an immense bundle of firewood, which he threw down before the cavern's mouth. He then drove into the cave the sheep and goats to be milked, and, entering, rolled to the cave's mouth an enormous rock, that twenty oxen could not draw. Next he sat down and milked his ewes, preparing a part for cheese, and setting the rest aside for his customary drink. Then turning round his great eye he discerned the strangers, and growled out to them, demanding who they were, and where from. Ulysses replied most humbly, saying that they were Greeks, from the great expedition that had lately won so much glory in the conquest of Troy; that they were now on their way home, and finished by imploring his hospitality in the name of the gods. Polyphemus deigned no answer, but reaching out his hand seized two of the Greeks, whom he hurled against the side of the cave, and dashed out their brains. He proceeded to devour them with great relish, and having made a hearty meal, stretched himself out on the floor to sleep. Ulysses was tempted to seize the opportunity and plunge his sword into him as he slept, but recollected that it would only expose them all to certain destruction, as the rock with which the giant had closed up the door was far beyond their power to remove, and they would therefore be in hopeless imprisonment. Next morning the giant seized two more of the Greeks, and despatched them in the same manner as their companions, feasting on their flesh till no fragment was left. He then moved away the rock from the door, drove out

his flocks, and went out, carefully replacing the barrier after him.
When he was gone Ulysses planned how he might take vengeance
for his murdered friends, and effect his escape with his surviving
companions. He made his men prepare a massive bar of wood
cut by the Cyclopes for a staff, which they found in the cave. They
sharpened the end of it and seasoned it in the fire, and hid it under
the straw on the cavern floor. Then four of the boldest were selected, with whom Ulysses joined himself as a fifth. The Cyclopes
came home at evening, rolled away the stone, and drove in his flock
as usual. After milking them and making his arrangements as
before, he seized two more of Ulysses' companions and dashed their
brains out, and made his evening meal upon them as he had on the
others. After he had supped, Ulysses, approaching him, handed
him a bowl of wine, saying: "Cyclopes, this is wine; taste and drink
after thy meal of man's flesh." He took and drank it all, was
hugely delighted with it, and called for more. Ulysses supplied him
once and again, which pleased the giant so much that he promised
him as a favor that he should be the last of the party devoured.
He asked his name, to which Ulysses replied, "My name is Noman."

After his supper the giant lay down to repose, and was soon sound
asleep. Then Ulysses with his four select friends thrust the end
of the stake into the fire till it was all one burning coal, then poising
it exactly above the giant's only eye, they buried it deeply in the
socket, twirling it around as a carpenter twirls his auger. The
howling monster with his outcry filled the cavern, and Ulysses with
his aids nimbly got out of his way and concealed themselves in the
cave. He, bellowing, called aloud on all the Cyclopes dwelling in
the caves around him, far and near. They on his cry flocked round
the den, and inquired what grievous hurt had caused him to sound
such an alarm and break their slumbers. He replied: "O friends,
I die, and Noman gives the blow." They answered: "If no man
hurts thee it is the stroke of Jove, and thou must bear it." So
saying, they left him groaning.

Next morning the Cyclops rolled away the stone to let his flock
out to pasture, but planted himself in the door of the cave to feel
of all as they went out, that Ulysses and his men should not escape
with them. But Ulysses had made his men harness the rams of the
flock three abreast, with osiers which they found on the floor of the
cave. To the middle ram of the three one of the Greeks suspended

himself, so protected by the exterior rams on either side. As they passed, the giant felt of the animals' backs and sides, but never thought of their bellies; so the men all passed safe, Ulysses himself being on the last one that passed. When they had got a few paces from the cavern, Ulysses and his friends released themselves from their rams, and drove a good part of the flock down to the shore to their boat. They put them aboard with all haste, then pushed off from the shore, and when at a safe distance Ulysses shouted out: "Cyclopes, the gods have well requited thee for thy atrocious deeds. Know it is Ulysses to whom thou owest thy shameful loss of sight." The Cyclopes, hearing this, seized a rock that projected from the side of the mountain, and rending it from its bed he lifted it high in the air, then exerting all his force, hurled it in the direction of the voice. Down came the mass, just clearing the vessel's stern. The ocean, at the plunge of the huge rock, heaved the ship toward the land, so that it barely escaped being swamped by the waves. When they had with the utmost difficulty pulled offshore, Ulysses was about to hail the giant again, but his friends besought him not to do so. He could not forbear, however, letting the giant know that they had escaped his missile, but waited till they had reached a safer distance than before. The giant answered them with curses, but Ulysses and his friends plied their oars vigorously, and soon regained their companions.

Ulysses next arrived at the island of Æolus. To this monarch Jupiter had entrusted the government of the winds, to send them forth or retain them at his will. He treated Ulysses hospitably, and at his departure gave him, tied up in a leathern bag with a silver string, such winds as might be hurtful and dangerous, commanding fair winds to blow the barks toward their country. Nine days they sped before the wind, and all that time Ulysses had stood at the helm, without sleep. At last, quite exhausted, he lay down to sleep. While he slept, the crew conferred together about the mysterious bag, and concluded it must contain treasures given by the hospitable King Æolus to their commander. Tempted to secure some portion for themselves, they loosed the string, when immediately the winds rushed forth. The ships were driven far from their course, and back again to the island they had just left. Æolus was so indignant at their folly that he refused to assist them further, and they were obliged to labor over their course once more by means of their oars.

The Læstrygonians. Their next adventure was with the barbarous tribe of Læstrygonians. The vessels all pushed into the harbor, tempted by the secure appearance of the cove, completely landlocked; only Ulysses moored his vessel without. As soon as the Læstrygonians found the ships in their power they attacked them, heaving huge stones, which broke and overturned them, and with their spears despatched the seamen as they struggled in the water. All the vessels with their crews were destroyed, except Ulysses's own ship, which had remained outside, and finding no safety but in flight, he exhorted his men to ply their oars vigorously, and they escaped.

With grief for their slain companions, mixed with joy at their own escape, they pursued their way till they arrived at the Ææan isle, where dwelt Circe, daughter of the sun. Landing here, Ulysses climbed a hill, and gazing round saw no signs of habitation except in one spot at the center of the island, where he perceived a palace embowered with trees. He sent forward one half of his crew, under the command of Eurylochus, to see what prospect of hospitality they might find. As they approached the palace, they found themselves surrounded by lions, tigers, and wolves, not fierce, but tamed by Circe's art, for she was a powerful magician. All these animals had once been men, but had been changed by Circe's enchantments into the forms of beasts. The sounds of soft music were heard from within, and a sweet female voice singing. Eurylochus called aloud, the goddess came forth and invited them in, and they all gladly entered except Eurylochus, who suspected danger. The goddess conducted her guests to a seat, and had them served with wine and other delicacies. When they had feasted heartily, she touched them one by one with her wand, and they became immediately changed into swine, in "head, body, voice, and bristles," yet with their intellects as before. She shut them in her sties and supplied them with acorns and such other things as swine love.

Eurylochus hurried back to the ship and told the tale. Ulysses thereupon determined to go himself, and try whether by any means he might deliver his companions. As he strode onward alone, he met a youth who addressed him familiarly, appearing to be acquainted with his adventures. He announced himself as Mercury, and informed Ulysses of the arts of Circe, and of the danger of approaching her. As Ulysses was not to be dissuaded from his attempt, Mercury provided him with a sprig of the plant Moly, of wonderful power to resist sorceries, and instructed him how to act. Ulysses proceeded, and reaching the palace was courteously received by Circe, who entertained him as she had entertained his companions, and after he had eaten and drunk, touched him with her wand, saying: "Hence: seek the sty and wallow with thy friends." But he, instead of obeying, drew his sword and rushed upon her with fury in his countenance. She fell on her knees and begged for mercy. He dictated a solemn oath that she would release his companions and practise no further harm against him or them; and she repeated it, at the same time promising to dismiss them all in safety after hospitably entertaining them. She was as good as her word. The men were restored to their shapes, the rest of the crew were summoned from the shore, and all were magnificently entertained day after day, till Ulysses seemed to have forgotten his native land, and to have reconciled himself to an inglorious life of ease and pleasure.

At last his companions recalled him to nobler sentiments, and he received their admonition gratefully. Circe aided their departure, and instructed them how to pass safely by the coast of the Sirens. The Sirens were sea-nymphs who had the power of charming by their song all who heard them, so that the unhappy mariners were irresistibly impelled to cast themselves into the sea to their destruction. Circe directed Ulysses to fill the ears of his seamen with wax, so that they should not hear the strain; and to cause himself to be bound to the mast, and his people to be strictly enjoined, whatever he might say or do, by no means to release him till they should have passed the Sirens' island. Ulysses obeyed these directions. He filled the ears of his people with wax, and suffered them to bind him with cords firmly to the mast. As they approached the Sirens' island, the sea was calm, and over the waters came the notes of music so ravishing and attractive that Ulysses struggled to get loose, and by cries and signs to his people begged to be released; but they, obedient to his previous orders, sprang forward and bound him still faster. They held on their course, and the music grew fainter till it ceased to be heard, when with joy Ulysses gave his companions the signal to unseal their ears, and they relieved him from his bonds.

Scylla and Charybdis. Ulysses had been warned by Circe of the two monsters, Scylla and Charybdis. Scylla was a snaky monster that used to seize sailors from passing vessels. Charybdis was a gulf, nearly on a level with the water. Thrice each day the water rushed into a frightful chasm, and thrice was disgorged. Any vessel coming near the whirlpool when the tide was rushing in must inevitably be engulfed; not Neptune himself could save it.

On approaching the haunt of the monsters, Ulysses kept strict watch to discover them. The roar of the waters as Charybdis engulfed them, gave warning at a distance, but Scylla could nowhere be discerned. While Ulysses and his men watched with anxious eyes the dreadful whirlpool, they were not equally on their guard from the attack of Scylla, and the monster, darting forth her snaky heads, caught six of his men, and bore them away shrieking to her den. It was the saddest sight Ulysses had yet seen—to behold his friends thus sacrificed and hear their cries, unable to afford them any assistance.

Circe had warned him of another danger. After passing Scylla and Charybdis the next land he would make was Thrinakia, an island whereon were pastured the cattle of Hyperion, the Sun, tended by his daughters, Lampetia and Phaëthusa. These flocks must not be violated, whatever the wants of the voyagers might be. If this injunction were transgressed, destruction was sure to fall on the offenders.

Ulysses would willingly have passed the island of the Sun without stopping, but his companions so urgently pleaded for the rest and refreshment that would be derived from anchoring and passing the night on shore that Ulysses yielded. He bound them, however, with an oath that they would not touch one of the animals of the sacred flocks and herds, but content themselves with what provision remained of the supply that Circe had put on board. So long as this supply lasted, the people kept their oath; but contrary winds detained them at the island for a month, and after consuming all their stock of provisions, they were forced to rely upon the birds and fishes they could catch. Famine pressed them, and at last one day, in the absence of Ulysses, they slew some of the cattle, vainly attempting to make amends for the deed by offering from them a portion to the offended powers. Ulysses, on his return to the shore, was horror-struck at perceiving what they had done, and the more so on account of the portentous signs that followed. The skins crept on the ground, and the joints of meat lowed on the spits while roasting.

The wind becoming fair, they sailed from the island. But they had not gone far when the weather changed and a thunderstorm ensued. A stroke of lightning shattered their mast, which in its fall killed the pilot. At last the vessel itself came to pieces. The keel and mast floating side by side, Ulysses formed of them a raft, to which he clung, and, the wind changing, the waves bore him to Calypso's island. All the rest of the crew perished.

Calypso. Calypso, a sea-nymph, received Ulysses hospitably, entertained him magnificently, became enamored of him, and wished to retain him forever, conferring on him immortality. But he persisted in his resolution to return to his country and his wife and son. Calypso at last received the command of Jove to dismiss him. Mercury brought the message to her and found her in her grotto. Calypso, with much reluctance, proceeded to obey the commands of Jupiter. She supplied Ulysses with the means of constructing a raft, provisioned it well, and gave him a favoring gale. He sped on his course prosperously for many days, till at last, when he was in sight of land, a storm arose that broke his mast and threatened to rend the raft asunder. In this crisis he was seen by a compassionate sea-nymph, who in the form of a cormorant alighted on the raft, and presented him a girdle, directing him to bind it beneath his breast, and if he should be compelled to trust himself to the waves, it would buoy him up and enable him by swimming to reach the land.

The Phæacians. Ulysses clung to the raft as long as any of its timbers kept together, and when it no longer yielded him support, binding the girdle around him, he swam. Minerva smoothed the billows before him and sent him a wind that rolled the waves toward the shore. The surf beat high on the rocks and seemed to forbid approach; but at last, finding calm water at the mouth of a gentle stream, he landed, spent with toil, breathless and speechless, almost dead. After some time, reviving, he kissed the soil, rejoicing, yet at a loss what course to take. At a short distance he perceived a wood, to which he turned his steps. There finding a covert sheltered by intermingling branches alike from the sun and the rain, he collected a pile of leaves and formed a bed, on which he stretched himself, heaped the leaves over him, and fell asleep.

The land where he was thrown was Scheria, the country of the Phæacians. These people dwelt originally near the Cyclopes; but being oppressed by that savage race they migrated to the isle of

Scheria, under the conduct of Nausithoüs, their king. They were akin to the gods, who appeared manifestly and feasted among them when they offered sacrifices, and did not conceal themselves from solitary wayfarers when they met them. They had abundance of wealth and lived in the enjoyment of it undisturbed by the alarms of war, for as they dwelt remote from gain-seeking men, no enemy ever approached their shores, and they did not even require to make use of bows and quivers. Their chief employment was navigation. Their ships, which went with the velocity of birds, were endued with intelligence; they knew every port, and needed no pilot. Al-cinoüs, the son of Nausithoüs, was now their king, a wise and just sovereign, beloved by his people.

It happened that the very night on which Ulysses was cast ashore on the Phæacian island, and while he lay sleeping on his bed of leaves, Nausicaa, daughter of the King, had a dream sent by Minerva, reminding her that her wedding-day was not far distant, and that it would be but a prudent preparation for that event to have a general washing of the clothes of the family. This was no slight affair, for the fountains were at some distance and the garments must be carried thither. On awaking, the Princess hastened to her parents to tell them what was on her mind; not alluding to her wedding-day, but finding other reasons equally good. Her father readily assented, and ordered the grooms to furnish forth a wagon for the purpose. The clothes were put therein, and the Queen-mother was placed in the wagon, likewise an abundant supply of food and wine. The Princess took her seat and plied the lash, her attendant virgins fol-lowing on foot. Arrived at the riverside, they turned out the mules to graze, and, unlading the carriage, bore the garments down to the water, and working with cheerfulness and alacrity soon despatched their labor. Then, having spread the garments on the shore to dry, and having themselves bathed, they sat down to enjoy their meal; after which they rose and amused themselves with a game of ball, the Princess singing to them while they played. But when they had refolded the apparel and were about to resume their way to the town, Minerva caused the ball thrown by the Princess to fall into the water, whereat they all screamed, and Ulysses awaked at the sound.

He was utterly destitute of clothing, and discovered that only a few bushes were interposed between him and a group of young

there the race of Æneas shall dwell, and reduce all other nations to their sway." The Trojans heard with joy, and immediately began to ask one another, "Where is the spot intended by the oracle?" Anchises remembered that there was a tradition that their fore-fathers came from Crete, and thither they resolved to steer. They arrived at Crete, and began to build their city, but sickness broke out among them, and the fields that they had planted failed to yield a crop. In this gloomy aspect of affairs, Æneas was warned in a dream to leave the country and seek a western land, called Hesperia, whence Dardanus, the true founder of the Trojan race, had origi-nally migrated. To Hesperia, now called Italy, therefore, they directed their course, but not till after many adventures and the lapse of time sufficient to carry a modern navigator several times round the world did they arrive there.

Their first landing was at the island of the Harpies. These were disgusting birds, with the heads of maidens, with long claws and faces pale with hunger. They were sent by the gods to torment a certain Phineus, whom Jupiter had deprived of his sight in punish-ment of his cruelty; and whenever a meal was placed before him, the Harpies darted down from the air and carried it off. They were driven away from Phineus by the heroes of the Argonautic expedi-tion, and took refuge in the island where Æneas now found them.

When they entered the port the Trojans saw herds of cattle roam-ing over the plain. They slew as many as they wished, and pre-pared for a feast. But no sooner had they seated themselves at the table than a horrible clamor was heard in the air, and a flock of these odious Harpies came rushing down upon them, seizing in their talons the meat from the dishes and flying away with it. Æneas and his companions drew their swords and dealt vigorous blows among the monsters, but to no purpose, for they were so nimble it was almost impossible to hit them, and their feathers were like armor impenetrable to steel. One of them, perched on a neighboring cliff, screamed out: "Is it thus, Trojans, you treat us innocent birds, first slaughter our cattle, and then make war on ourselves?" She then predicted dire sufferings to them in their future course, and, having vented her wrath, flew away. The Trojans made haste to leave the country, and next found themselves coasting along the shore of Epirus. Here they landed, and to their astonishment learned that certain Trojan exiles, who had been carried there as prisoners, had become rulers of the country. Andromache, the widow of Hector, became the wife of one of the victorious Grecian chiefs, to whom she bore a son. Her husband dying, she was left regent of the country, as guardian of her son, and had married a fellow captive, Helenus, of the royal race of Troy. Helenus and Andromache treated the exiles with the utmost hospitality, and dismissed them loaded with gifts.

Thence Æneas coasted along the shore of Sicily, and passed the country of the Cyclopes. Here they were hailed from the shore by a miserable object, whom by his garments, tattered as they were, they perceived to be a Greek. He told them he was one of Ulysses's companions, left behind by that chief in his hurried departure. He related the story of Ulysses's adventure with Polyphemus, and besought them to take him off with them, as he had no means of sustaining his existence where he was, but wild berries and roots, and lived in constant fear of the Cyclopes. While he spoke Polyphemus made his appearance; a terrible monster, shapeless, vast, whose only eye had been put out. He walked with cautious steps, feeling his way with a staff, down to the seaside, to wash his eye-socket in the waves. When he reached the water, he waded out toward them, and his immense height enabled him to advance far into the sea, so that the Trojans, in terror, took to their oars to get out of his way. Hearing the oars, Polyphemus shouted after them, so that the shores resounded, and at the noise the other Cyclopes came forth from their caves and woods, and lined the shore, like a row of lofty pine-trees. The Trojans plied their oars, and soon left them out of sight.

Æneas had been cautioned by Helenus to avoid the strait guarded by the monsters Scylla and Charybdis. There Ulysses had lost six of his men, seized by Scylla, while the navigators were wholly intent upon avoiding Charybdis. Æneas, following the advice of Helenus, shunned the dangerous pass and coasted along the island of Sicily.

Juno, seeing the Trojans speeding their way prosperously toward their destined shore, felt her old grudge against them revive, for she could not forget the slight that Paris had put upon her in awarding the prize of beauty to another. In heavenly minds can such resentments dwell! Accordingly, she hastened to Æolus, the ruler of the winds—the same who supplied Ulysses with favoring gales, giving him the contrary ones tied up in a bag. Æolus obeyed the goddess and sent forth his sons, Boreas, Typhon, and the other winds to toss the ocean. A terrible storm ensued, and the Trojan ships were driven out of their course toward the coast of Africa. They were in imminent danger of being wrecked, and were separated, so that Æneas thought that all were lost except his own.

At this crisis Neptune, hearing the storm raging and knowing that he had given no orders for one, raised his head above the waves and saw the fleet of Æneas driving before the gale. Knowing the hostility of Juno, he was at no loss to account for it, but his anger was not the less at this interference in his province. He called the winds, and dismissed them with a severe reprimand. He then soothed the waves, and brushed away the clouds from before the face of the sun. Some of the ships which had got on the rocks he pried off with his own trident, while Triton and a sea-nymph, putting their shoulders under others, set them afloat again. The Trojans, when the sea became calm, sought the nearest shore, which was the coast of Carthage, where Æneas was so happy as to find that one by one the ships all arrived safe, though badly shaken.

Queen Dido. Carthage, where the exiles had now arrived, was on the coast of Africa opposite Sicily, where at that time a Tyrian colony under Dido, their Queen, were laying the foundations of a state, destined in later ages to be the rival of Rome itself. Dido was the daughter of Belus, King of Tyre, and sister of Pygmalion, who succeeded his father on the throne. Her husband was Sichæus, a man of immense wealth, but Pygmalion, who coveted his treasures, caused him to be put to death. Dido, with a numerous body of friends and followers, men and women, succeeded in effecting their escape from Tyre, in several vessels, carrying with them the treasures of Sichæus. On arriving at the spot which they selected as the seat of their future home, they asked of the natives only so much land as they could enclose with a bull's hide. When this was readily granted, Dido caused the hide to be cut into strips, and with them enclosed a spot on which she built a citadel, and called it Byrsa (a hide). Around this fort the city of Carthage rose, and it soon became a powerful and flourishing place.

Such was the state of affairs when Æneas with his Trojans arrived there. Dido received the illustrious exiles with friendliness and hospitality. "Not unacquainted with distress," she said, "I have learned to succor the unfortunate." The Queen's hospitality displayed itself in festivities, at which games of strength and skill were exhibited. The strangers contended for the palm with her own subjects, on equal terms, the Queen declaring that whether the victor were Trojan or Tyrian should make no difference to her. At the feast that followed the games, Æneas gave at her request a recital of the closing events of the Trojan history and his own adventures after the fall of the city. Dido was charmed with his discourse and filled with admiration of his exploits. She conceived an ardent passion for him, and he for his part seemed well content to accept the fortunate chance, which appeared to offer him at once a happy termination of his wanderings—a home, a kingdom, and a bride. Months rolled away in the enjoyment of pleasant intercourse, and it seemed as if Italy and the empire destined to be founded on its shores were alike forgotten. Seeing which, Jupiter despatched Mercury with a message to Æneas recalling him to a sense of his high destiny, and commanding him to resume his voyage.

Æneas parted from Dido, though she tried every allurement and persuasion to detain him. The blow to her affection and her pride was too much for her to endure, and when she found that he was gone, she mounted a funeral pile that she had caused to be prepared, and, having stabbed herself, was consumed with the pile. The flames rising over the city were seen by the departing Trojans, and, though the cause was unknown, gave to Æneas some intimation of the fatal event.

Palinurus. After touching at the island of Sicily, where Acestes, a prince of Trojan lineage, bore sway, who gave them a hospitable reception, the Trojans reembarked, and held on their course for Italy. Venus now interceded with Neptune to allow her son at last to attain the wished-for goal and find an end of his perils on the deep. Neptune consented, stipulating only for one life as a ransom for the rest. The victim was Palinurus, the pilot. As he sat watching the stars, with his hand on the helm, Somnus sent by Neptune, approached in the guise of Phorbas, and said: "Palinurus, the breeze is fair, the water smooth, and the ship sails steadily on her course. Lie down awhile and take needful rest. I will stand at the helm in your place." Palinurus replied, "Tell me not of smooth seas or favoring winds—me who have seen so much of their treachery. Shall I trust Æneas to the chances of the weather and the winds?" And he continued to grasp the helm and to keep his eyes fixed on the stars. But Somnus waved over him a branch moistened with Lethæan dew, and his eyes closed in spite of all his efforts. Then Somnus pushed him overboard and he fell; but keeping his hold upon the helm, it came away with him. Neptune was mindful of his promise and kept the ship on her track without helm or pilot, till Æneas discovered his loss, and sorrowing deeply for his faithful steersman took charge of the ship himself.

The ships at last reached the shores of Italy. While his people were making their encampment Æneas sought the abode of the Sibyl. It was a cave connected with a temple and grove, sacred to Apollo and Diana. While Æneas contemplated the scene, the Sibyl accosted him. She seemed to know his errand, and, under the influence of the deity of the place, burst forth in a prophetic strain, giving dark intimations of labors and perils through which he was destined to make his way to final success. She closed with the encouraging words that have become proverbial: "Yield not to disasters, but press onward the more bravely." Æneas replied that he had prepared himself for whatever might await him. He had but one request to make. Having been directed in a dream to seek the abode of the dead in order to confer with his father Anchises to receive from him a revelation of his future fortunes and those of his race, he asked her assistance to enable him to accomplish the task. The Sibyl replied: "The descent to Avernus is easy; the gate of Pluto stands open night and day; but to retrace one's steps and return to the upper air, that is the toil, that the difficulty." She instructed him to seek in the forest a tree on which grew a golden branch. This branch was to be plucked off and borne as a gift to Proserpine, and if fate was propitious it would yield to the hand and quit its parent trunk, but otherwise no force could rend it away. If it were torn away, another would succeed.

Æneas followed the directions of the Sibyl. His mother Venus sent two of her doves to fly before him and show him the way, and by their assistance he found the tree, plucked the branch, and hastened with it to the Sibyl.

The Infernal Regions. The lake Avernus is supposed to fill the crater of an extinct volcano. It is circular, half a mile wide, and very deep, surrounded by high banks. Here was the cave that afforded access to the infernal regions, and here Æneas offered sacrifices to the infernal deities, Proserpine, Hecate, and the Furies.

Then a roaring was heard in the earth, the woods on the hilltops were shaken, and the howling of dogs announced the approach of the deities. "Now," said the Sibyl, "summon up your courage, for you will need it." She descended into the cave, and Æneas followed. Before the threshold of hell they passed through a group of beings who are enumerated as Griefs and avenging Cares, pale Diseases and melancholy Age, Fear and Hunger that tempt to crime, Toil, Poverty, and Death, forms horrible to view. The Furies spread their couches there, and Discord, whose hair was of vipers tied up with a bloody fillet. Here also were the monsters, Briareus with his hundred arms, Hydras hissing, and Chimæras breathing fire. Æneas shuddered at the sight, drew his sword and would have struck, but the Sibyl restrained him. They then came to the black river Cocytus, where they found the ferryman, Charon, old and squalid, but strong and vigorous, who was receiving passengers of all kinds into his boat, magnanimous heroes, boys and unmarried girls, as numerous as the leaves that fall at autumn, or the flocks that fly southward at the approach of winter. They stood pressing for a passage and longing to touch the opposite shore. But the stern ferryman took in only such as he chose, driving back the rest. Æneas wondering at the sight, asked the Sibyl, "Why this discrimination?" She answered: "Those who are taken on board the bark are the souls of those who have received due burial rites; the host of others who have remained unburied are not permitted to pass the flood, but wander a hundred years, and flit to and fro about the shore, till at last they are taken over." Æneas grieved at recollecting some of his own companions who had perished in the storm. At that moment he beheld Palinurus, his pilot, who fell overboard and was drowned. He asked him the cause of his misfortune. Palinurus replied that the rudder was carried away, and he, clinging to it, was swept away with it. He besought Æneas most urgently to extend to him his hand and take him in company to the opposite shore. The Sibyl rebuked him for the wish thus to transgress the laws of Pluto, but consoled him by informing him that the people of the shore where his body had been wafted by the waves should be stirred up by prodigies to give it due burial, and that the promontory should bear the name of Cape Palinurus, which it does to this day. Leaving Palinurus consoled by these words, they approached the boat. Charon, fixing his eyes sternly upon the advancing warrior, demanded by what right he, living and armed, approached that shore. To which the Sibyl replied that they would commit no violence, that Æneas's only object was to see his father, and finally exhibited the golden branch, at sight of which Charon's wrath relaxed, and he made haste to turn his bark to the shore and receive them on board. The boat, adapted only to the light freight of bodiless spirits, settled under the weight of the hero. They were soon conveyed to the opposite shore. There they were encountered by the three-headed dog Cerberus, with his necks bristling with snakes. He barked with all his three throats till the Sibyl threw him a medicated cake, which he eagerly devoured, and then stretched himself out in his den and fell asleep.

Æneas and the Sibyl sprang to land. The first sound that struck their ears was the wailing of young children, who had died on the threshold of life, and near to these were they who had perished under false charges. Minos presides over them as judge, and examines the deeds of each. The next class was of those who had died by their own hand, hating life and seeking refuge in death. Next were situated the regions of sadness, divided off into retired paths, leading through groves of myrtle. Here roamed those who had fallen victims to unrequited love, not freed from pain even by death itself. Among these Æneas thought he descried the form of Dido, with a wound still recent. In the dim light he was for a moment uncertain, but approaching, perceived it was indeed herself. Tears fell from his eyes, and he addressed her in the accents of love. "Unhappy Dido! was then the rumor true that you had perished? and was I, alas! the cause? I call the gods to witness that my departure from you was reluctant, and in obedience to the commands of Jove; nor could I believe that my absence would have cost you so dear. Stop, I beseech you, and refuse me not a last farewell." She stood for a moment with averted countenance and eyes fixed on the ground, and then silently passed on, as insensible to his pleadings as a rock. Æneas followed for some distance; then, with a heavy heart, rejoined his companion and resumed his route.

They next entered the fields where roam the heroes who have fallen in battle. Here they saw many shades of Grecian and Trojan warriors. The Trojans thronged around him, and could not be satisfied with the sight. They asked the cause of his coming, and plied him with innumerable questions. But the Greeks, at the sight of his armor glittering through the murky atmosphere, recognized the hero, and, filled with terror, turned their backs and fled, as they used to do on the plains of Troy.

Æneas would have lingered long with his Trojan friends, but the Sibyl hurried him away. They next came to a place where the road divided, the one leading to Elysium, the other to the regions of the condemned. Æneas beheld on one side the walls of a mighty city, around which Phlegethon rolled its fiery waters. Before him was the gate of adamant that neither gods nor men can break through. An iron tower stood by the gate, on which Tisiphone, the avenging Fury, kept guard. From the city were heard groans, and the sound of the scourge, the creaking of iron, and the clanking of chains. Æneas, horror-struck, inquired of his guide what crimes were those whose punishments produced the sounds he heard? The Sibyl answered: "Here is the judgment-hall of Rhadamanthus, who brings to light crimes done in life, which the perpetrator vainly thought impenetrably hid. Tisiphone applies her whip of scorpions, and delivers the offender over to her sister Furies." At this moment, with horrid clang the brazen gates unfolded, and Æneas saw within a Hydra with fifty heads guarding the entrance. The Sibyl told him that the gulf of Tartarus descended deep, so that its recesses were as far beneath their feet as heaven was high above their heads. In the bottom of this pit the Titan race, who warred against the gods, lie prostrate; Salmoneus, also, who presumed to vie with Jupiter, and built a bridge of brass over which he drove his chariot that the sound might resemble thunder, launching flaming brands at his people in imitation of lightning, till Jupiter struck him with a real thunderbolt, and taught him the difference between mortal weapons and divine. Here, also, is Tityus, the giant, whose form is so immense that, as he lies, he stretches over nine acres, while a vulture preys upon his liver, which as fast as it is devoured grows again, so that his punishment will have no end.

Æneas saw groups seated at tables loaded with dainties, while near by stood a Fury who snatched away the viands from their lips as fast as they prepared to taste them. Others beheld suspended over their heads huge rocks, threatening to fall, keeping them in a state of constant alarm. These were they who had hated their brothers, or struck their parents, or defrauded the friends who trusted them, or who, having grown rich, kept their money to them-

destined leader must come from across the sea. They have offered the crown to me, but I am too old to undertake such great affairs, and my son is native-born, which precludes him from the choice. You, equally by birth and time of life, and fame in arms, pointed out by the gods, have but to appear to be hailed at once as their leader. With you I will join Pallas, my son, my only hope and comfort. Under you he shall learn the art of war, and strive to emulate your great exploits."

Then the King ordered horses to be furnished for the Trojan chiefs, and Æneas, with a chosen band of followers and Pallas accompanying, mounted and took the way to the Etruscan city, having sent back the rest of his party in the ships. Æneas and his band safely arrived at the Etruscan camp and were received with open arms by Tarchon and his countrymen.

Nisus and Euryalus. In the mean while Turnus had collected his bands and made all necessary preparations for the war. Juno sent Iris to him with a message inciting him to take advantage of the absence of Æneas and surprise the Trojan camp. Accordingly the attempt was made, but the Trojans were found on their guard, and having received strict orders from Æneas not to fight in his absence, they lay still in their entrenchments, and resisted all the efforts of the Rutulians to draw them into the field. Night coming on, the army of Turnus, in high spirits at their fancied superiority, feasted and enjoyed themselves, and finally stretched themselves on the field and slept secure.

In the camp of the Trojan things were far otherwise. There all was watchfulness and anxiety, and impatience for Æneas's return. Nisus stood guard at the entrance of the camp, and Euryalus, a youth distinguished above all in the army for graces of person and fine qualities, was with him. These two were friends and brothers in arms. Nisus said to his friend: "Do you perceive what confidence and carelessness the enemy display? Their lights are few and dim, and the men seem all oppressed with wine or sleep. You know how anxiously our chiefs wish to send to Æneas and to get intelligence from him. Now I am strongly moved to make my way through the enemy's camp and to go in search of our chief. If I succeed, the glory of the deed will be reward enough for me, and if they judge the service deserves anything more, let them pay it to you."

Euryalus, all on fire with the love of adventure, replied: "Would you then, Nisus, refuse to share your enterprise with me? And shall I let you go into such danger alone? Not so my brave father brought me up, nor so have I planned for myself when I joined the standard of Æneas, and resolved to hold my life cheap in comparison with honor." Nisus replied: "I doubt it not, my friend; but you know the uncertain event of such an undertaking, and whatever may happen to me I wish you to be safe. You are younger than I and have more of life in prospect. Nor can I be the cause of such grief to your mother, who has chosen to be here in the camp with you rather than stay and live in peace with the other matrons in Acestes's city." Euryalus replied: "Say no more. In vain you seek arguments to dissuade me. I am fixed in the resolution to go with you. Let us lose no time." They called the guard, and committing the watch to them, sought the general's tent. They found the chief officers in consultation, deliberating how they should send notice to Æneas of their situation. The offer of the two friends was gladly accepted, themselves loaded with praises, and promised the most liberal rewards in case of success. Iulus especially addressed Euryalus, assuring him of his lasting friendship. Euryalus replied: "I have but one boon to ask. My aged mother is with me in the camp. For me she left the Trojan soil, and would not stay behind with the other matrons at the city of Acestes. I go now without taking leave of her. I could not bear her tears nor set at naught her entreaties. But do thou, I beseech you, comfort her in her distress. Promise me that, and I shall go more boldly into whatever dangers may present themselves." Iulus and the other chiefs were moved to tears, and promised to do all his request. "Your mother shall be mine," said Iulus, "and all that I have promised to you shall be made good to her, if you do not return to receive it."

The two friends left the camp and plunged at once into the midst of the enemy. They found no watch, no sentinels posted, but all about the sleeping soldiers strewn on the grass and among the wagons. The laws of war at that early day did not forbid a brave man to slay a sleeping foe, and the two Trojans slew, as they passed, such of the enemy as they could without exciting alarm. In one tent Euryalus made prize of a helmet brilliant with gold and plumes. They had passed through the enemy's ranks without being discovered, but now suddenly appeared a troop directly in front of them, which, under Volscens, their leader, were approaching the camp. The glittering helmet of Euryalus caught their attention, and Volscens hailed the two, and demanded who and whence they were. They made no answer, but plunged into the wood. The horsemen scattered in all directions to intercept their flight. Nisus had eluded pursuit and was out of danger, but Euryalus being missing he turned back to seek him. He again entered the wood and soon came within sound of voices. Looking through the thicket he saw the whole band surrounding Euryalus with noisy questions. What should he do? How extricate the youth, or would it be better to die with him?

Raising his eyes to the moon, which now shone clear, he said, "Goddess! favor my effort!" and, aiming his javelin at one of the leaders of the troop, struck him in the back and stretched him on the plain with a death-blow. In the midst of their amazement, another weapon flew and another of the party fell dead. Volscens, the leader, ignorant whence the darts came, rushed sword in hand upon Euryalus. "You shall pay the penalty of both," he said, and would have plunged the sword into his bosom, when Nisus, who from his concealment saw the peril of his friend, rushed forward, exclaiming: "'Twas I, 'twas I; turn your swords against me, Rutulians; I did it; he only followed me as a friend." While he spoke the sword fell and pierced the comely bosom of Euryalus. His head fell over on his shoulder, like a flower cut down by the plow. Nisus rushed upon Volscens and plunged his sword into his body, and was himself slain on the instant by numberless blows.

Mezentius. Æneas, with his Etrurian allies, arrived on the scene of action in time to rescue his beleaguered camp; and now the two armies being nearly equal in strength, the war began in good earnest. The tyrant Mezentius, finding himself engaged against his revolted subjects, raged like a wild beast. He slew all who dared to withstand him, and put the multitude to flight wherever he appeared. At last he encountered Æneas, and the armies stood still to see the issue. Mezentius threw his spear, which striking Æneas's shield, glanced off and hit Anthor. He was a Grecian by birth, who had left Argos, his native city, and followed Evander into Italy. Æneas now in turn hurled his lance. It pierced the shield of Mezentius, and wounded him in the thigh. Lausus, his son, could not bear the sight, but rushed forward and interposed himself, while the followers pressed round Mezentius and bore him away. Æneas held his sword suspended over Lausus and delayed to strike, but the furious youth pressed on and he was compelled to deal the fatal blow. Lausus fell, and Æneas bent over him in pity. "Hapless youth," he said, "what can I do for you worthy of your praise? Keep those arms in which you glory, and fear not but that your body shall be restored to your friends and have due funeral honors." So saying, he called the timid followers and delivered the body into their hands.

Mezentius meanwhile had been borne to the riverside, and washed his wound. Soon the news reached him of Lausus's death, and rage and despair supplied the place of strength. He mounted his horse and dashed into the thickest of the fight, seeking Æneas. Having found him, he rode round him in a circle, throwing one javelin after another, while Æneas stood fenced with his shield, turning every way to meet them. At last, after Mezentius had three times made the circuit, Æneas threw his lance directly at the horse's head. It pierced his temples and he fell, while a shout from both armies rent the skies. Mezentius asked no mercy, but only that his body might be spared the insults of his revolted subjects, and be buried in the same grave with his son.

Pallas, Camilla, Turnus. While these things were doing in one part of the field, in another Turnus encountered the youthful Pallas. The contest between champions so unequally matched could not be doubtful. Pallas bore himself bravely, but fell by the lance of Turnus. The victor almost relented when he saw the brave youth lying dead at his feet, and spared to use the privilege of a conqueror in despoiling him of his arms. The belt only, adorned with studs and carvings of gold, he took and clasped round his own body. The rest he remitted to the friends of the slain.

After the battle there was a cessation of arms for some days to allow both armies to bury their dead. In this interval Æneas challenged Turnus to decide the contest by single combat, but Turnus evaded the challenge. Another battle ensued, in which Camilla, the virgin warrior, was chiefly conspicuous. Her deeds of valor surpassed those of the bravest warriors, and many Trojans and Etruscans fell pierced with her darts or struck down by her battle-ax. At last an Etruscan named Aruns, who had watched her long, seeking for some advantage, observed her pursuing a flying enemy whose splendid armor offered a tempting prize. Intent on the chase she observed not her danger, and the javelin of Aruns struck her and inflicted a fatal wound. She fell and breathed her last in the arms of her attendant maidens. But Diana, who beheld her fate, suffered not her slaughter to be unavenged. Aruns, as he stole away, glad but frightened, was struck by a secret arrow, launched by one of the nymphs of Diana's train, and died ignobly and unknown.

At last the final conflict took place between Æneas and Turnus. Turnus had avoided the contest as long as he could, but impelled by the ill success of his arms, and by the murmurs of his followers, he braced himself to the conflict. It could not be doubtful. On the side of Æneas were the expressed decree of destiny, the aid of his goddess-mother at every emergency, and impenetrable armor fabricated by Vulcan, at her request, for her son. Turnus, on the other hand, was deserted by his celestial allies, Juno having been expressly forbidden by Jupiter to assist him any longer. Turnus threw his lance, but it recoiled harmless from the shield of Æneas. The Trojan hero then threw his, which penetrated the shield of Turnus and pierced his thigh. Then Turnus's fortitude forsook him and he begged for mercy; and Æneas would have given him his life, but at the instant his eye fell on the belt of Pallas, which Turnus had taken from the slaughtered youth. Instantly his rage revived, and exclaiming, "Pallas immolates thee with this blow," he thrust him through with his sword.

Æneas, having triumphed over his foes, obtained Lavinia for his bride. Tradition adds that he founded his city, and called it after her name, Lavinium. His son Iulus founded Alba Longa, which was the birthplace of Romulus and Remus and the cradle of Rome itself.

Elysium. Virgil places his Elysium under the earth, and assigns it for a residence to the spirits of the blessed. But Homer's Elysium forms no part of the realms of the dead. He places it on the west of the earth, near Ocean, and describes it as a happy land, where there is neither snow, nor cold, nor rain, always fanned by the delightful breezes of Zephyrus. Hither favored heroes pass without dying and live happy under the rule of Rhadamanthus. The Elysium of Hesiod and Pindar is in the Isles of the Blessed, or Fortunate Islands, in the Western Ocean. From these sprang the legend of the happy island Atlantis.

Oracles. Oracle was the name used to denote the place where answers were supposed to be given by any of the divinities to those who consulted them respecting the future. The word was also used to signify the response that was given.

The most ancient Grecian oracle was that of Jupiter at Dodona. According to one account it was established in the following manner. Two black doves took their flight from Thebes in Egypt. One flew to Dodona in Epirus, and, alighting in a grove of oaks, it proclaimed in human language to the inhabitants of the district that they must establish there an oracle of Jupiter. The other dove flew to the temple of Jupiter Ammon in the Libyan Oasis and delivered a similar command there. Another account is, that they were not doves, but priestesses, who were carried off from Thebes in Egypt by the Phenicians, and set up oracles at the Oasis and Dodona. The responses of the oracle were given from the trees, by the branches rustling in the wind, the sounds being interpreted by the priests.

But the most celebrated of the Grecian oracles was that of Apollo at Delphi, a city built on the slopes of Parnassus in Phocis. It had been observed at a very early period that the goats feeding on Parnassus were thrown into convulsions when they approached a certain long, deep cleft in the side of the mountain. This was owing to a peculiar vapor arising out of the cavern, and one of the goatherds was induced to try its effects upon himself. Inhaling the intoxicating air, he was affected in the same manner as the cattle had been, and the inhabitants of the surrounding country, unable to explain the circumstance, imputed the convulsive ravings, to which he gave utterance while under the power of the exhalations, to a divine inspiration. The fact was speedily circulated widely, and a temple was erected on the spot. The prophetic influence was assigned to Apollo. A priestess was appointed, whose office it was to inhale the hallowed air, and who was named the Pythia. She was prepared for this duty by previous ablution at the fountain of Castalia, and being crowned by laurel was seated upon a tripod similarly adorned, which was placed over the chasm whence the divine afflatus proceeded. Her inspired words while thus situated were interpreted by the priests.

The oracle of Trophonius in Bœotia was held in high estimation. Trophonius and Agamedes were brothers. They were distinguished architects, and built the temple of Apollo at Delphi, and a treasury for King Hyrieus. In the wall of the treasury they placed a stone in such a manner that it could be taken out, and by this means from time to time purloined the treasure. This amazed Hyrieus, for his locks and seals were untouched, and yet his wealth continually diminished. At last he set a trap for the thief, and Agamedes was caught. Trophonius, unable to extricate him, and fearing that when found he would be compelled by torture to discover his accomplice, cut off his head. Trophonius himself is said to have been shortly afterward swallowed up by the earth.

The oracle of Trophonius was at Lebadea in Bœotia. At the time of a great drought the Bœotians, it is said, were directed by the god at Delphi to seek aid of Trophonius at Lebadea. They came thither, but could find no oracle. One of them, however, happening to see a swarm of bees, followed them to a chasm in the earth, which proved to be the place sought. Peculiar ceremonies were to be performed by the person who came to consult the oracle. After these preliminaries, he descended into the cave by a narrow passage. This place could be entered only in the night. The person returned from the cave by the same narrow passage, but walking backward.

There were numerous oracles of Æsculapius, but the most celebrated was at Epidaurus. Here the sick sought responses and the recovery of their health by sleeping in the temple. It has been inferred from the accounts that have come down to us that the treatment of the sick resembled what is now called animal magnetism or mesmerism. Serpents were sacred to Æsculapius, probably because of a superstition that those animals have a faculty of renewing their youth by a change of skin. The worship of Æsculapius was introduced into Rome in a time of great sickness, and an embassy was sent to the temple of Epidaurus to entreat the aid of the god. Æsculapius was propitious, and on the return of the ship accompanied it in the form of a serpent. Arriving in the river Tiber, the serpent glided from the vessel and took possession of an island in the river, and a temple was there erected to his honor.

At Memphis the sacred bull Apis gave answer to those who consulted him, by the manner in which he received or rejected what was presented to him. If the bull refused food from the hand of the inquirer, it was considered an unfavorable sign, and the contrary when he received it.

PART V.

SCANDINAVIAN MYTHOLOGY

The Creation. In the beginning of time a world existed in the north called Niflheim, in the middle of which was a well, from which flowed twelve rivers. In the south there was another world, a flaming and radiant world, the boundary of which was guarded by Surt with a flaming sword. Cold and heat contended with each other. From Niflheim flowed cold, poisonous streams, which froze so that one layer of ice was piled upon another in the Ginnunga-gap, the abyss that faced the north; but from the south flowed heat, and the sparks shone so that the south part of the abyss was light. The heat met the ice, and the drops of the melting ice received life, and a human form came forth, called Ymir, father of the Frost Giants. Ymir was not a god, but was evil, together with all his race. There was as yet neither sand nor sea, nor cool waves, neither earth, nor grass, nor vaulted heaven, but only the abyss. Ymir was nourished by four streams of milk which flowed from the cow Audhumla, a creature made by Surt. Ymir gave birth to children while he slept; for having fallen into a sweat, from under his left arm there grew a man and woman, and one of his feet begat a son by the other. The cow licked the frost-covered stones that were salt, and the first day toward evening there came forth from them a man's hair, the second day a head, the third day an entire man. He was called Buri, and was tall, strong, and handsome. His son Bor married Bestla, and their three sons were Odin, Vili, and Ve. These brothers were gods and created heaven and earth. Bor's sons slew the giant Ymir, and there ran so much blood from his wound that all the Frost Giants were drowned in it except the giant Bergeluir, who escaped with his wife on a chest and continued the race of frost-giants. Bor's sons carried the body of Ymir into Ginnunga-gap, and formed of it the earth, of his blood the seas and waters, of his bones the mountains; of his teeth and grinders and those bones that were broken they made stones and pebbles; from the blood that flowed from his wounds they made the great, impassable ocean, in which they fixed the earth, around which it lies in a circle; of his skull they formed the heaven, and set it up over the earth with four regions, and under each corner placed a dwarf. Of his brain they formed the heavy clouds, of his hair the vegetable creation, and of his eyebrows a wall of defense against the giants around Midguard, the midmost part of the earth, the dwelling-place of the sons of men. They then took the sparks and glowing cinders that were cast out of Muspelheim, and set them in heaven, both above and below, to illumine heaven and earth. They also assigned places for the lightning and fiery meteors, some in heaven, and some unconfined under heaven, and appointed to them a course. Hence came the division of years and days. Bor's sons raised up the heavenly disks so that the sun shone on the cold stones, and all the earth was decked with green herbs. The sun from the south followed the moon and cast her right arm around the east, but she knew not where her dwelling lay, and the moon knew not his power, nor did the stars know where they had a station. Then the holy gods consulted together and gave to every light its place, and a name to the new moon, and to the waning moon, and gave names to the morning and the midday, and the evening, that the children of men, the sons of Time, might reckon the years afterward.

Night and Day were of opposite races. Night, of giant race, was dark, like her father. She was married to Anar, and their daughter was the Earth. Then she married Delling, and their son was Day, who was fair, bright, and beautiful, like his father. All-Father, who was among the Frost Giants before heaven and earth existed, gave Night and Day horses and cars, and placed them in heaven that they might ride behind each other, in twenty-four hours' time, around the earth. Night rides first with her horse, which bedews the earth with the drops from his bit. From the shining mane of Day's horse light beams forth o'er heaven and earth. The Moon and Sun are brother and sister on account of their beauty. Mundilfori, their father, calls his son, the Moon, Mani, and his daughter, the Sun, Sol. Sol married a man named Glen, and her horses are called Watchful and Rapid, and the gods send an ice-cool breeze to fan them. There is also a cooling shield before the sun, else the sea and the mountains would be set on fire.

There are two wolves, one of which follows the sun, and the sun
fears that it will swallow her. The other runs before the sun and
strives to seize on the moon, and so, in the end, it will be. The
mother of these wolves is a giantess who dwells in a wood to the east
of Midguard, and her many sons are giants in the form of wolves.
The most powerful of these lives upon the dying. He will finally
swallow up the moon, and thus sprinkle heaven and earth with blood.
Then the sun will lose its brightness, and the winds rage and howl
in all directions. But winter and summer shall reign every year
until the gods pass away. At the end of heaven sits the giant Hraes-
velg, in an eagle's garb, and from the moving of his wings comes the
final breath.

The Destruction of Earth. Loki, the all-powerful, lay under
the hot spring's grove. In the iron forest east of Midguard the
old giantess brought forth the progeny of Fenrir (the deep); one,
named Skoll, will pursue the sun to the encircling ocean; the other
will run before the sun and will swallow up the moon. He will be
sated with the lives of the dying. On a height will sit the dauntless
eagle and strike his harp. Over him, in the Bird-wood, will crow the
light red cock. Over the Æsir will crow the gold-combed cock that
wakens heroes in Odin's hall. But a soot-red cock will crow beneath the earth, in Hel's abode. Loudly will howl the dog Garm;
bonds will be burst, the wolf will run forth, brothers will contend
and slay each other, kindred tear kindred's bond asunder. Great
abominations there shall be—an ax-tide, a sword-tide, a wind-tide,
a wolf-tide—ere the world perishes; no man will spare another.
The tree of knowledge shall be burned. Midguard's serpent shall
put on his giant mood, and plow through the billowy deep; from
the south comes Surt with flickering flames; the stone mountains
crack, the giantesses stumble, men tread the way to Hel, and heaven
is riven. Then shall Thor, the glorious son of Odin, go against
the Midguard's serpent and shall bravely slay it. Then shall all
men forsake their home, the world. The sun shall be darkened,
the earth sink in ocean, the stars vanish from heaven, smoky clouds
encircle the all-nourishing tree, high flames play against heaven
itself. There will come a winter when snow will drift from every
side; the sun will lose its power. One wolf will swallow up the
sun, the other wolf will seize the moon.

But when these things take place, Heimdall will stand up **and** blow his horn with all his might, and rouse up every god to hold a meeting. Odin will ride first with his golden helmet and bright corselet, and with his spear. He will encounter the wolf Fenrir. Thor will be at his side, but he cannot help him, as he will be fighting the Midguard serpent, which he gains glory by slaying. After all this Surt will hurl fire over the earth and burn the whole world.

There will arise, a second time, an earth from ocean, in verdant beauty. Waterfalls will descend, and the eagle fly over the mountain streams. The Æsir will meet again on Ida's plain, and speak of the mighty earth-encircler. There will they remember the great deeds of old, and the ancient lore of the glorious gods. Then will they find in the grass the wonderful golden tables, which at Time's origin the prince of the gods possessed. Unsown fields shall then bear fruit, and all evil cease. There will be an orb mightier than the sun, and there virtuous folk shall dwell and enjoy happiness forever more. Then will the Mighty One come to the gods' council, powerful from above, He who rules all things; He will pronounce judgments, appease quarrels, and establish peace that shall last forever.

Huldra (*Norwegian*). Huldra, the Fairy, dwells both in the forests and in the hills. She seems a beautiful woman and wears generally a sky-blue petticoat and a snow-white snood. It is her great misfortune to possess a long tail, like a cow's, which she is always trying to hide. She loves cattle and owns some beautiful ones herself. They are harmless, as they have no horns. Once she was at a rural frolic, and everybody wanted to dance with the beautiful stranger, but just as she was whirling merrily with a handsome youth, he caught sight of her appendage. He was dismayed, for he well knew who his partner must be, but he was so gallant that he did not wish to betray her, so he said to her as the dance ended: "Fair maiden, you will lose your garter." This gave her excuse for vanishing, but she afterward rewarded the young man with presents, among which was a fine stock of cattle. The description of Huldra differs very much in different parts of Norway. Sometimes she is pictured as having only a front, the back being hollow. Sometimes she is said to be blue herself, but dressed in green. She is a songstress, and her airs are mournful and hollow-sounding, heard generally among the mountains. In this she is different from the underworld folk, whose music is always cheerful and fascinating.

Dwarfs and Trolls (*Norwegian*). The underground folk of Norway are believed by the natives to be very numerous. The dwarfs and elves live under forests and meadows, and the trolls under mountains and hills. They have houses, churches, cattle, which graze at night under care of faithful dog-watchers and of girls. The dwarfs are thought to be well-formed, but to have a blue complexion. After sunset their activity begins. Then it is dangerous for anybody, but especially for young women, to pass by the places which they frequent, and where exquisite music can be heard to steal forth. Many instances are told where young girls have been carried away and hidden in forest or mountain.

They are often believed to leave a changeling child instead of a stolen one, and the little one pines away. To prevent such calamity a cross or a piece of steel is laid in the cradle of infants. It is said that when God cast down the fallen angels from heaven, some fell into hell; but some, who had not sinned so deeply, were spread abroad through earth and air and sea, and these form the fairy underworld.

Jutuls (*Norwegian*). The Jutuls are large and strong and have their dwelling in the highest mountains, where riches and costly treasure are to be found in plenty. A Jutul has an evil heart and he hates churches and the sound of bells, and is a cannibal, living on Christian blood. When there is a storm brewing, or a whirlwind among the mountains, he is said to be shaking himself, so that his pots and kettles resound, as his wife prepares his food. All over the land may be seen the footprints of this giant pair, and the stories of their work are endless. They are the most ancient of all mythical beings of the north. As giants they ruled over the cold, dark regions of earth, shunning the sunlight, which changed them to stone.

On Hestmandoe in the Nordlands there is a mountain, which at a distance resembles a horseman with a large cloak about him. This mountain was once a Jutul, who dwelt on the spot. Twelve miles to the south, on Lekoe in Nummedal, lived at the same time a maiden to whom he made love; but the damsel, who was haughty and was versed in all kinds of magic, not only rejected him, but turned all his messengers to stone, who are still to be seen as rocks round the northern part of the isle. Exasperated at such conduct, the Jutul bent his bow. to take a ferocious vengeance. The

but each time the boat glided back. In the third attempt, at the upper part of the fall, the priest dashed his hand into the water and drew out something that looked like a little black dog. He ordered the men to keep on rowing up, while he held the animal firmly between his feet and kept perfectly quiet. When he reached the stone mound at Tvet he recited a ban over the Nok and since then no one has perished at that waterfall. The Nok's relative, the Fossegrine, also lives by the waterfalls and he plays a musical instrument after dark on still evenings. If, on a Thursday evening, a person with averted face will offer him a kid he will be taught to play. For a lean kid he will be taught to tune the instrument, but for a fat one the Fossegrine seizes the player's hand and passes it across the instrument until the blood comes. After this, the adventurer can play in such a wonderful manner that the trees will dance and the waterfalls stop flowing to listen.

The Qværnknurre (*Norwegian*). In Gierrestad it was formerly the custom to place a soft loaf, a cup of beer, or something of the kind by the millstone in order that the Qværnknurre might increase the flour in the sacks. For some time he took up his abode in the Sandager waterfall, where a man had a mill. As often as the man began to grind corn the mill stopped. Knowing that it was the Qværnknurre that was doing the mischief, he took some pitch in a pot over a fire and set his mill going. When it stopped, as usual, he thrust down a pole to see if he could rid himself in that way. This was of no avail, and as he opened the door in a hopeless way, lo! there stood the Qværnknurre opening a mouth of such size that the jaws reached from the top to the bottom of the doorway. "Hast thou ever seen such great gaping?" said the creature. "Hast thou ever tasted such hot pitch?" said the miller, and threw the contents of the boiling pot into the extended jaws, whereupon the creature vanished with a howl, and was never seen again.

Gertrud's Bird (*Norwegian*). When our Lord, accompanied by St. Peter, was wandering on earth, they came to a woman who was occupied in baking; her name was Gertrud, and she wore a red hood on her head. Weary and hungry from long journeying, our Lord asked for one of her cakes. She took a little dough and set it on to bake, and it grew so large that it filled the whole pan. Thinking that too much to give away, she took a smaller quantity of dough, and again began to bake, but that swelled up to the same size as the first; she then took still less dough, and when the cake became as large as the others, Gertrud said: "You must go without alms, for all my bakings are too large for you." Then was our Lord wroth, and said: "Because thou givest me nothing, thou shalt become a little bird, shalt seek thy dry food between the wood and the bark, and drink only when it rains." Hardly had he spoken when the woman was transformed into the Gertrud's Bird, and flew away through the kitchen chimney, and at this day she is seen with a red hood and a black body, because she was blackened by the soot of the chimney. She is constantly pecking the bark of trees for food, and whistling for rain that she may quench her thirst.

Thor (*Swedish*). Thor, as well as Odin, was said to have come to the North with an immigration from Asgard. Here he had to contend with the land's earliest inhabitants, who from their dwelling in mountain caverns and dens, as well as from their gigantic stature and ferocity, were called giants, trolls, Bergsboar. Hence all the traditions about giants and such folk have a similar origin. Those smooth, wedge-shaped stones which are sometimes found in the earth are called thorwiggar, and are said to have been hurled at a troll by Thor. When it thundered the trolls were terrified and came rolling down the mountainside, sometimes in one shape and sometimes in another, generally like large balls. They sought shelter among the mowers, but the mowers were afraid of their arts and would keep them off with their scythes, and when the lightning struck and shivered the scythe the troll, with a piteous piping sound, would return to the mountain.

It is related that about a hundred years ago some sailors for Bohuslan, while out in a Dutch ship from Amsterdam, on the whale fishery near Greenland, being driven out of their course, for many nights observed the light of a fire from an island or shore, at which they were seized with a desire to visit the place and see who the people were; so they took the ship's boats and rowed to the spot. Having landed and approached the fire they saw an old man sitting and warming himself, who immediately asked whence they came.

"From Holland," answered the man from Bohuslan.

"But from what place art thou, thyself?" inquired the old man.

"From Safve on Hisingen," answered the sailor.

"Art thou acquainted with Thorsby?"

"Yes, well."

"Dost thou know where the Ulfveberg is?"

"Yes, I have often passed it, because there is a direct way from Gothenborg to Marstrand across Hisingen through Thorsby."

"Do the great stones and the earth-mounds still stand in their places?"

"Yes, all but one stone, which is ready to fall."

"Tell me further," said the old heathen; "dost thou know where Glosshed's altar is, and whether it is still safe and sound?"

When the sailor answered that it was not, the old man said: "Wilt thou desire the people in Thorsby and Thores-bracka not to destroy the stones and mounds under the Ulfveberg, and above all things to keep the altar at Glosshed safe and whole, so shalt thou have a good wind to the place for which thou art bound." All this the sailor promised to perform on his return home. On asking the old man his name, and why he so anxiously inquired about such objects, he answered: "My name is Thorer Brack, and my habitation is there; but I am now a fugitive. In the great mound by the Ulfvesberg my whole race lies buried, and at Glosshed's altar we performed our worship to the gods." They parted from the old man and under a fair wind reached their home.

Odin (*Swedish*). In Bleking it was formerly the custom to leave a sheaf of wheat for Odin's horses. In Kraktorpsgard a barrow was opened in which Odin was said to have been buried. In it was found a vault from which a wondrous fire, like a lightning flash, burst forth. A coffin of flint, also, and a lamp, were found at the same place and time. It is related that Peter Dagson, a priest who dwelt near Troienborg, planted some rye, and when it grew Odin came riding over the hills every evening, so lofty of stature that he towered above the buildings in the farmyard, and waved his spear in his hand. Stopping before the entrance, he hindered everyone during the whole night from going out or coming in. And this happened every night until the rye was cut.

The Severed Hand (*Norwegian*). There was once a miller whose mill was burned down on two successive Whitsun-eves. In the third year, just before Whitsuntide, he had a tailor in his house to make holiday clothes.

"I wonder how it will go with the mill this time; whether it will be burned again to-night," said the miller.

"You need not fear that," said the tailor; "give me the key and I will watch in it."

This seemed to the miller both good and highly acceptable, and when it drew toward evening the tailor got the key and went to the mill, which was still empty, having just been rebuilt. So placing himself in the middle of the floor, he chalked around him a large circle, on the outside of which he wrote the Paternoster; and thus fortified, would not have feared if the arch-enemy himself had made his appearance. In the dead of the night the door suddenly flew open, and in came such a multitude of black cats that the place literally swarmed. But a short time had elapsed before they set a large earthen pot in the chimney and lighted a fire under it, so that it began frying and hissing as if it were full of boiling pitch and tar.

"Oho," thought the tailor. "Is that what you are after?" And hardly had he given utterance to the thought when one of the cats put its paw behind the pot and tried to upset it.

"Whisht, cat, you'll burn yourself!" cried the tailor.

"Whisht, cat, you'll burn yourself, the tailor says," cried the cat to the other cats, and all ran from the chimney and began dancing and hopping around the circle, but the cat again sneaked to the chimney and tried to upset the pot.

"Whisht, cat, you'll burn yourself," cried the tailor, and drove it from the chimney.

"Whisht, cat, you'll burn yourself, the tailor says," said the cat to the other cats, and all began dancing and hopping again, but in a moment the same cat tried a third time to overturn the pot.

"Whisht, cat, you'll burn yourself!" cried the tailor in a rage, and so terrified them that they tumbled over one another and began to jump and dance as before. They formed a circle outside the tailor's circle, and danced around it with ever-increasing velocity, until at length it seemed to the tailor that everything was whirling around before him. All this time the cats were staring at him with their large, fierce eyes as if they would swallow him.

While they were in the thick of this, the cat that had tried to upset the pot put her paw within the circle, as if she felt inclined to seize hold of the tailor, but he, seeing her design, drew out his knife and stood on his guard. After a few moments the cat again put her paw within the ring, when the tailor instantly chopped it off, and all the cats took to their heels, screaming and howling, as speedily as they could, and left the tailor in quiet possession of the field.

The tailor lay down within his circle till long after the sun had been shining in upon him. He then rose, locked the mill door, and proceeded to the miller's house. When he entered the room the miller and his wife were still in their bed, it being Whit-Sunday.

"Good morning," said the tailor, giving the miller his hand.

"Good morning," said the miller in return, and was both glad and surprised to see the tailor again.

"Good morning, mother," said he, holding out his hand to the miller's wife.

"Good morning," said she, but appeared pale and sorrowful, and kept her hand under the bedclothes, but at last she offered him her left hand. The tailor now saw how matters stood; but nothing is told of what afterward took place.

St. Olaf (*Norwegian*). As St. Olaf was one day wandering among the woods and mountains meditating deeply as to how he could accomplish the construction of a church without laying heavy burdens on his people and yet erect a building of such magnitude that its like could not be found, he met a man of gigantic size who asked him what he was pondering upon. "I may well be pondering," replied the King, "having made a vow to build a church which shall be without its like in the whole world for magnitude and magnificence."

The troll thereupon undertook to complete such a structure by a certain fixed time, but only on condition that if the work should be finished within the given time St. Olaf would promise to give, as remuneration, the sun and moon, or St. Olaf himself.

The King agreed to the condition because he fancied that he could plan such a vast edifice that it would be impossible even for the giant to build it in the time agreed upon. It was to be so spacious that seven priests might preach in it at the same time without hearing or disturbing one another. The pillars and ornaments, both without and within, were to be of the hardest flint; besides which were many other equally difficult conditions. But within a much shorter time than that specified, the King saw his church completed, all except the spire, which was still to be erected. Seeing this, the saint went out again to wander in the woods and mountains in deep tribulation, thinking of his unfortunate promise, when suddenly he heard a child crying and saw a giantess comforting it with the following song:

> "Hush, hush, my son,
> To-morrow comes Wind and Tempest, thy father,
> And he has with him sun and moon
> Or St. Olaf himself."

Now the King was overjoyed, because trolls, as we are told, always lose their power when a Christian man calls them by their name. On his return he saw the giant standing on the top of the tower, in the act of placing the spire, and he called to him:

> "Wind and Tempest,
> Thou hast set the spire awry."

From the summit of the church the troll fell with a terrific smash and was shivered in fragments, all of which were flint.

The Bridal Elf (*Swedish*). It is believed that all brides are subject to the envy of the underworld folk, and the bridegroom is cautioned to lay in his clothing certain herbs as a counter-charm. Near gates and crossways the elves are said to lie in wait. The bride is pictured as ready in the bridal bower, surrounded by her bridesmaids. The bridegroom is pictured saddling his gray steed, in knightly attire, after which, with hawk on perch, he rides forth from his mother's hall to bring home his bride. But in the wood he has hunted hides a jealous elf, chanting a melody of surpassing sweetness. As he draws near the elf-mount, or enters the castle-gate, the strains become so ravishing that he is fain to pause a moment to listen. This is the time that was waited for, and the elf-king's daughter steps out of the dancing ring and beckons him to have one merry round upon the turf before he renounces his freedom. If he yields, he is instantly borne to Elfland, and he wanders about amid gardens and music more beautiful than his wildest picture. At length, perchance, thought of his deserted betrothed enters his mind, and the elves assist him back to the home he begins to pine for. But, lo! all is changed. The time which he believed to be but a moment is many years. Everything is altered, and his betrothed long before had died of grief.

The Mermaid (*Swedish*). In certain lakes are strange beings called Spokvatten, or Water-specters. When warmed by the sun these specters send up a mist, snow-white, sometimes resembling a human form, and sometimes that of an animal. It changes its course and appearance as it is driven by the wind. The mermaid usually sits by the lake and combs her long, golden hair with a golden comb. Sometimes she stands on the islets and spreads her snowy linen on the bushes, or drives her snow-white cattle before her. She has a dangerous reputation, for she is believed to be false and treacherous, and the sight of her presages tempest and shipwreck. No sailor speaks of the vision to his comrade if he has caught sight of the witching and terrible maiden, but he takes his steel and flint and strikes fire, as the sign of home and the hearthstone makes her powerless for evil. From the time that Thor hurled his thunder at the trolls they lost power and courage, but a light must be kept on every hearthstone, or a light burn day and night until after a new-born child is christened, or the mermaids may come and steal the child from its cradle and leave one of their own in its stead. The mermaids' own home at the bottom of the sea or lake has houses and castles and cattle and domestic animals. There is a lake with beautifully wooded shores, called Lake Anten. It bears an island, where formerly stood a castle, now in ruins. There dwelt Sir Gunner, a renowned knight, and once, when out on the lake, he fell into danger. A mer-wife rescued him, but extracted the promise that he would meet her again at the same place. On a Thursday evening she sat waiting, but he had forgotten his promise and did not go. In her rage she caused the lake to rise and to flood the cattle. Sir Gunner sought safety in the higher apartments, but the water rose. He sought the drawbridge tower, but here the waves chased him. He entered a boat, but instantly sank, like a stone. There, to this day, can be seen Gunner's Stone, while he lives far below with the mer-wife.

In passing the spot sailors lift their hats respectfully to Sir Gunner and trust that the reward of their civility will be good fortune.

The Bergtroll (*Swedish*). The name of a person or an animal is sacred or is evil, as the case may be. If you abuse a cat, you must not use her name, because she belongs to the Bergtroll in the mountains, where she visits them. The cuckoo, the owl, and the magpie are better not called by name. Neither they nor the snakes should be carelessly killed, because they have powerful magic allies that may avenge them. It is wrong to kill toads by stepping on them, because they are not infrequently princesses held by enchantment.

Many a person has become lame because he has wantonly hurt a toad. If you mention a troll-pack you must first name the name "fire," "water," your church. In this way you ward off all harm. The animals may be designated by the names that describe them or their supposed habits. You may call the wolf gold-foot, but not Varg, as the old rhyme says:

> "If thou callest me Varg, I will be wroth with thee,
> But if thou callest me *of gold*, I will be kind to thee."

And not animals alone, but inanimate things have a fastidious feeling about their names. Fire does not like to be called *eld*, but *hetta*— heat. The water used in brewing must be *lag*, and not *vatn*, or the beer will be sour. But of all creatures, the magpie is the most to be dealt cautiously with. On Walpurgis night the witches change themselves to magpies and ride to Blakulle. When the magpies moult and lose their neck feathers it is commonly said that they have been to Blakulle and helped the devil to get in his hay, and his yoke has rubbed the feathers off.

Halvar's Room (*Swedish*). In the district of Nas in Warmland the children have a stone playhouse. Once there lived in it a giant who was on good terms with a farmer near by. One day when the farmer and another man returned from their work, they found the giant sitting outside the stone room. "Can I trade with thee?" said the giant. "Seven goats will I give thee for a cow." The farmer consented, and the following morning his wife was greatly surprised to find when she went to the cow-house that the cow was gone, and there were seven goats in her place. The bargain proved excellent, and the goats brought them good luck.

One Easter eve, the farmer was passing, when the giant, who was sitting on his stone seat, said: "Wilt thou come in and eat milk porridge with me?"

"No," replied the farmer. "If thou hast more than thou canst eat, keep it till to-morrow."

"Thanks," said the giant. "Had I known that before, I should now have been rich." But the giant disappeared, and the farmer received no more favors.

Axel Thordsen and **Fair Valdborg** (*Norwegian*). In the land of Norway in former days lived a maiden so fair that she was universally called Fair Valdborg. Her father, Sir Immer, died in her infancy,

way, Slaugerop! I am going to a little water yonder, and then I hope to be a better man."

The House Nisse (*Danish*). In a farmhouse in Jutland there was a Nisse, who every evening got his porridge in proper time, and therefore helped both man and maid, and saw to his master's interest in every way possible. But there finally entered into the master's service a mischievous boy, who took every opportunity to annoy the Nisse, and one night when all were gone to rest, and the Nisse had taken his little wooden bowl and was about to enjoy his evening meal, he discovered that the boy had hidden the butter at the bottom, in order to make him eat his porridge first and then find the butter. Whereupon he determined to take revenge on the boy, and he stole up to the loft where the boy was sleeping beside the hired man. He took off the coverlet, and seeing the tall man and the short boy by his side, he began pulling the boy's legs down to make them even with the man's. Then he went to the head of the bed and pulled him up to the man's head. He kept repeating this process till he was tired, and then he crept up and seated himself in the window-sill. Dogs have a great aversion to Nisser, and, as it grew light, and the dogs in the yard saw him, they set up a great barking, at which the Nisse was very much amused, because he was beyond their reach. He put out first one little foot and then the other, saying, "Look at this little trotter," "Look at that little trotter." The bad boy woke, and seeing the Nisse and hearing the noise he gave the little fellow a push, saying: "There, now look at him from top to toe."

Turning the Sieve (*North German*). During a time of war a butcher of Amnom, having more business than he could attend to alone, took a neighbor's son to help him. He placed so much confidence in the youth that he showed where his little hoard of money lay. This the son communicated to his mother, and both were seized with an irresistible desire to get possession of the money; so that on the following morning when the mother came for a pound or two of meat, the son contrived to place the bag containing the money in the bottom of her basket. Some days later, when the butcher discovered his loss, his suspicion immediately fell on his assistant; but the boy protested by all that was holy that he was innocent. There was at this time not far away a sorcerer, who could discover thieves and compel them to restore the stolen property.

The butcher sent his wife to the sorcerer, and he immediately began his enchantment. He took a flour-sieve, placed in it a key and a pair of scissors, and set it on a large vessel filled with water. He then uttered some magical sentences, and the woman pronounced the name of all the suspected persons. As often as she mentioned the name of her neighbor the key danced about; and when the sorcerer desired her to look into the water, she plainly saw her husband's assistant in the act of handing the money to his mother. But the sorcerer told her that it would not be possible to recover the money, because the thieves had already crossed the water with it.

The Devil's Cat (*North German*). A peasant had three beautiful, large cats. A neighbor begged to have one of them, and obtained it. To accustom it to the place he shut it up in a loft. At night the cat, popping its head through the window, said: "What shall I bring to-night?" "Thou shalt bring mice," answered the man. The cat then set to work and cast all it caught on the floor. Next morning the place was so full of dead mice that it was hardly possible to open the door, and the man was busy the whole day throwing them away by the bushel. At night the cat again put its head through the aperture and asked: "What shall I bring to-night?" "Thou shalt bring rye," answered the peasant. The cat was now busily employed in shooting down rye, so that in the morning the door could not be opened.

The man then saw that the cat was a witch, and carried it back to his neighbor, in which he acted prudently, to wit, in not saying the second time: "Thou shalt bring gold," for then he would have got as much gold as he did rye.

The people of Dousum are accounted sorcerers; the women in particular are all said to be witches. On this account no one cares to hold any intercourse with them, and no one marries outside of the village. On a Friday no woman is to be found at home because on that day they hold their meetings and have dances on the barren heath. In the evening they ride thither on horses, though usually they have wings on their shoulders and fly. In their flight they are often unable to stop at the right time, so that if a church steeple is in their way they fly against it. They can transform themselves into cats, and into horses; into swans and eagles.

Wind-Knots (*North German*). At Siseby on the Slei dwelt a woman who was a sorceress and could change the wind. The Sleswig

herring fishers used frequently to land there. Once when they wished
to return to Sleswig, the wind being west, they requested the woman
to change it. She agreed to do so for a dish of fish. She gave them
a cloth with three knots, telling them they might untie the first and
second, but not the third until they had reached land. The men
spread their sails, although the wind was west; but no sooner had
the oldest of the party undone the first knot than a beautiful, fair
wind came from the east. On undoing the second knot they had
a storm and reached their port with all speed. They were then
curious to know what would happen if they undid the third knot;
but no sooner had they done so than a hurricane arose from the
west, and they had to leap into the water to draw their boat ashore.

The Underworld Child (*North German*). Some young peasants
once resolved on catching one of the underworld folk. It is a
hard thing to do, as these people never appear by day and seldom
by night, but they waited until St. John's eve, and they lay in wait
very cleverly. The little creatures were nimble and their retreat
small and well hidden, so that they would all have escaped had not
a young man succeeded in catching a young girl by the apron. Full
of joy he carried the little maiden home to his wife, who put it in her
lap. They fed her sugar and all sorts of nice things, but could not
make her speak. The little creature neither ate nor drank nor
laughed nor cried. Finally, there came an old woman who advised
them to set about doing everything in the wrong way, for that was
what the underworld folk could not endure, and that would cause
her to speak. So the peasant wife told the little maid to wash the
pieces of turf nicely for soup, and to cut up the meat to light the fire.
The child did not move. So the woman washed the turf and then
began to cut the meat and make ready to light the fire with it.

"Woman, you surely will not sin against God?" said the child.

"Not if thou wilt speak," answered the woman. "If thou wilt
I will do everything right; else, wrong." From that time the little
one spoke, but not long after she made her escape, and when the
woman had a child of her own, a changeling was put in the cradle
in its place.

The Wild Huntsman (*North German*). A drunken peasant was
passing one night through a forest on his way from the town, when
he heard the Wild Hunt and the noise of the dogs and of the huntsmen in the air. "In the middle of the road! in the middle of

the road!" cried a voice, to which he gave no heed. On a sudden a tall man on a white horse precipitated himself from the clouds before him. "Art thou strong?" said he. "See which can pull the strongest. Here, take hold of this chain." The countryman took hold of the heavy chain, and the wild hunter soared toward the sky. The countryman wound the chain around an oak, and the huntsman tugged in vain. "Thou hast surely wound the chain round an oak," said Wod, descending. "No," said the countryman, who had hastily loosed it. "See, I am holding it in my hands." "Then thou shalt be mine up in the clouds," cried the huntsman, again mounting. The countryman quickly flung the chain again around the oak, and Wod was as unsuccessful as before. "But hast thou not fastened the chain around the oak?" said Wod, coming down again. "No," said the countryman. "See, I am holding it in my hands." "If thou wert heavier than lead thou must up with me in the clouds, notwithstanding." Saying this he darted up like lightning, but the countryman had recourse to the old process. The dogs barked, the carriages rolled, the horses neighed up aloft. The oak cracked at its roots and seemed to turn, but it held fast, while the countryman felt far from comfortable.

"Thou hast pulled capitally," said the huntsman. "Many men have I made mine; thou art the first that hast withstood me. I will reward thee." Loud was the uproar of the hunt. The countryman sneaked away toward home, when from an unseen height a deer fell dying before him, and there stood Wod, who, springing from his white horse, cut up the game. "The blood shalt thou have, and a haunch besides," said Wod. "Sir," said the countryman, "thy servant hath neither pail nor pitcher." "Take thy boot off," cried Wod. He did so. "Now march home with blood and flesh to wife and brat." Fear at first caused his burden to seem light, but by degrees it grew heavier and heavier, so that he could scarcely walk under it. Bent almost double, dripping with sweat, he at length reached his hut, and behold! the boot was full of gold, and the haunch turned out to be a bag full of silver.

The Man Without a Shadow (*North German*). Many preachers and sacristans visit the Black School where they are instructed in the Black Art, by means of which they can exorcise witches, specters, spirits, and even the devil himself, who taught them. The devil's only condition in return for his lessons is that the one who goes last out of the door, when the course is ended, shall belong to him. All his pupils think that they can outwit him, and many have done so. Among them was Brous, of Hadersleben. He was the last to leave the school, but he had played his part so cunningly that he could not be trapped. The school door was to the south, and it happened that the lecture was to be finished in bright sunshine, so that the sacristan informed the devil that not he, but his shadow, would be last to go out, and that the devil was welcome to keep. This was according to the devil's own teaching, so he could make no objection, and he let the man go and kept his shadow. From that time to this the sacristan has been shadowless, the brightest sunshine revealing not the sign of a shadow as he moves.

The Outwitted Witch (*North German*). In the neighborhood of Busum there dwelt a wealthy peasant who had an only daughter whom he tenderly loved. But his mother-in-law was a witch. People knew that on several occasions she had transformed herself into a cat or other animal; in companies, too, she had caused the whole room to be full of ravens, so that the guests were driven away. She grudged the peasant his good fortune, and at length decided to bewitch his daughter. She gave the girl a beautiful new dress, but when it was put on her hair suddenly stood on end, her eyes rolled, and she dashed herself against the doors and windows. She cried and raved at everybody, evidently not knowing them or what she did. When the fit passed she was exhausted and was with difficulty undressed and put to bed. From that time she dwindled in strength. The physicians could not help her or define her malady, and her parents were inconsolable. Some sagacious neighbor suggested that there was in Hamburg a man who could probably afford relief, and the father instantly set out to go there. After hearing the full account the man told the father that the trouble was certainly caused by witchcraft; that he would give him a pot of medicine which would probably afford relief if the father could reach home with the pot unbroken, but that the witches would make every effort to break it. The peasant gave the ship's boy the basket containing the pot to carry to land, when the sand rose like a waterspout and dashed the basket out of his hand, so that the pot was broken into a thousand fragments. The peasant returned to the doctor, who told him that he must delay two days and that then his task would be much more difficult than before. This time the doctor packed the pot carefully himself, and told the peasant to keep the strictest watch over it, adding that there was still one other method of saving his daughter, if this failed, but he should be reluctant to try it. This time the peasant went home by land, and so watchful was he that his carriage was in sight of his house when it was violently upset and the pot again smashed. He allowed himself no rest, and within twelve hours was again in Hamburg. The doctor told him that the only method remaining was to boil in oil the old witch who had done the mischief. Then began a series of spells and magic, and the doctor came back with a large mirror, in which the peasant recognized his mother-in-law. Knowing now the cause, and also knowing that either she or his daughter must die, he told the doctor to continue his work.

This consisted of spells over a kettle of boiling oil, and when the peasant returned to his home his daughter met him in perfect health, while he was shown a heap of burnt bones and ashes and learned that the mother-in-law had died the day before.

The Piper of Hameln (*North German*). In the year 1284 the town of Hameln was intolerably infested with rats. One day there came to the town a man most singularly clad, no one knew from whence, and offered to rid the town of rats for a certain sum of money.

The townsfolk were glad to promise the money, and thereupon the man drew forth a pipe and played upon it, and in an instant every rat in town came scrambling out of the buildings and sewers and followed the music in such numbers that the streets were choked with them. When he reached the river the man walked in and the rats, following, were drowned and their bodies washed down-stream. But no sooner were the people relieved of their distress than they repented of their promise to part with the money, and, on the plea that he was a sorcerer, they refused payment, and the piper was furious and vowed vengeance. On St. John's and St. Paul's day, when the elders were in church, he entered the town again, dressed as a huntsman, with a red hat. This time the tune he played fascinated the children so that they could not resist following and dancing to the melody. Slowly he passed through the gate to the Koppleberg Mountain, and when he reached it they all disappeared. A nursery maid reported that the mountain opened and closed again. Two boys remained behind, one who, as he was blind, could only tell what he heard, and the other who, as he was dumb, could only point to the place where his companions disappeared, and nothing was to be seen but a small hollow.

The Forgetful Smith (*North German*). In Juterbogle dwelt a smith whose father had brought him up with great care. He traveled much, was very skilful, had served as the Emperor's armorer, and been a successful soldier. Once, when he was over a hundred years old, he was sitting under a pear-tree when a little gray man whom the smith looked upon as his guardian spirit drew near and told him to make three wishes, but not to forget the best. The smith, annoyed by boys, wished that whoever climbed his pear-tree might not be able to come down, because thieves had lately robbed him; wished that no one might enter his house without permission, unless he came through the keyhole. Again the little gray man reminded his foolish friend not to forget the best wish, whereupon the silly fellow cried that he wanted the best schnapps, and that the flask might never be empty. The wishes were granted and, in addition, the smith was given silver enough to live in comfort. The flask contained an elixir of life, and Death seemed to have passed him by; but, at length, he knocked at his door. The smith said he was ready to go with him, but they ought to refresh themselves, and as he could no longer climb, he begged Death to go into the tree and hand down some pears. "There, stay," said the smith, when Death had climbed to the branches. Death, having eaten all the pears, fed upon his own flesh, and now appears a skeleton. No one died on earth, and it was found to be very inconvenient. At last the smith released him on promise not to be touched. Finally the smith grew completely tired of life, and he set out to find heaven. St. Peter looked out, but when he saw his visitor he said: "Get you hence. You forgot the best wish—for eternal happiness." Peter the smith then traveled the well-trod road to hell, but when the devil saw him he slammed the door in his face and placed his kingdom in a state of defense. The smith had no desire to return to the earth, but he finally sought his old master, Emperor Frederick, who inquired whether the ravens still flew about the old ruined castle of Kiffhausen. Hearing that they did, he heaved a sigh. The smith remained in the mountain shoeing the horses of the Emperor and his court—waiting till the hour strikes that brings deliverance to the Emperor, which will also be his own, when the ravens cease to circle around Kiffhausen and the withered pear-tree blossoms.

Starkad and His Sons (*Icelandic*). There was a man named Starkad; he was a son of Bork the waxy-toothed blade, the son of Thorkell Clubfoot, who took the land round about Threecorner as the first settler. His wife's name was Hallbera. The sons of Starkad and Hallbera were these: Thorgeir and Bork and Thorkell. Hildigunna the leech was their sister. They were very proud men in temper, hard-hearted and unkind. They treated men wrongfully.

There was a man named Egil; he was a son of Kol, who took land as a settler between Storlek and Reydwater. The brother of Egil was Aunund of Witchwood, father of Hall the strong, who was at the slaying of Holt-Thorir with the sons of Kettle the smooth-tongued. Egil kept house at Sandgil; his sons were these: Kol and Ottar and Hauk. Their mother's name was Steinvor; she was Starkad's sister. Egil's sons were tall and strifeful; they were most unfair men. They were always on one side with Starkad's sons. Their sister was Gudruna nightsun, and she was the best bred of women.

Egil had taken into his house two Easterlings; the one's name was Thorir and the other's Thorgrim. They were not long come out thither for the first time, and were wealthy and beloved by their friends; they were well skilled in arms, too, and dauntless in everything.

Starkad had a good horse of chestnut hue, and it was thought that no horse was his match in fight. Once it happened that these brothers from Sandgil were away under the Threecorner. They had much gossip about all the householders in the Fleetlithe, and they fell at last to asking whether there was anyone that would fight a horse against them. But there were some men there who spoke so as to flatter and honor them, that not only was there no one who would dare do that, but that there was no one that had such a horse.

Then Hildigunna answered: "I know that man who will dare to fight horses with you."

"Name him," they said.

"Gunnar has a brown horse," she said, "and he will dare to fight his horse against you, and against anyone else."

"As for you women," they said, "you think no one can be Gunnar's match; but though Geir the priest or Gizur the white has come off with shame from before him, still it is not settled that we shall fare in the same way."

"Ye will fare much worse," she said; and so out of this the greatest strife arose between them. Then Starkad said:

"My will is that ye try your hands on Gunnar last of all; for ye will find it hard work to go against his good luck."

"Thou wilt give us leave, though, to offer him a horse-fight?"

"I will give you leave, if ye play him no trick."

They said they would be sure to do what their father said.

Now they rode to Lithend; Gunnar was at home, and went out, and Kolskegg and Hjort went with him, and they gave him a hearty welcome, and asked whither they meant to go.

"No farther than hither," they said. "We are told that thou hast a good horse, and we wish to challenge thee to a horse-fight."

"Small stories can go about my horse," said Gunnar; "he is young and untried in every way."

"But still thou wilt be good enough to have the fight, for Hildigunna guessed that thou wouldst be easy in matching thy horse."

"How came ye to talk about that?" said Gunnar.

"There were some men," they said, "who were sure that no one would dare to fight his horse with ours."

"I would dare to fight him," said Gunnar; "but I think that was spitefully said."

"Shall we look upon the match as made, then?" they asked.

"Well, your journey will seem to you better if ye have your way in this; but still I will beg this of you, that we so fight our horses that we make sport for each other, but that no quarrel may arise from it, and that ye put no shame upon me; but if ye do to me as ye do to others, then there will be no help for it but that I shall give you such a buffet as it will seem hard to you to put up with. In a word, I shall do then just as ye do first."

Then they rode home. Starkad asked how their journey had gone off; they said that Gunnar had made their going good.

"He gave his word to fight his horse, and we settled when and where the horse-fight should be; but it was plain in everything that he thought he fell short of us, and he begged and prayed to get off."

"It will often be found," said Hildigunna, "that Gunnar is slow to be drawn into quarrels, but a hard hitter if he cannot avoid them."

Gunnar rode to see Njal, and told him of the horse-fight, and what words had passed between them. "But how dost thou think the horse-fight will turn out?"

"Thou wilt be uppermost," said Njal, "but yet many a man's bane will arise out of this fight."

"Will my bane perhaps come out of it?" asked Gunnar.

"Not out of this," said Njal; "but still they will bear in mind both the old and the new feud who fare against thee, and thou wilt have naught left for it but to yield."

Then Gunnar rode home. Just then Gunnar heard of the death of his father-in-law Hauskuld; a few nights after this Thorgerda, Thrain's wife, was delivered at Gritwater, and gave birth to a boy child. Then she sent a man to her mother, and bade her choose whether it should be called Glum or Hauskuld. She bade call it Hauskuld. So that name was given to the boy.

Gunnar and Hallgerda had two sons; the one's name was Hogni and the other's Grani. Hogni was a brave man of few words, distrustful and slow to believe, but truthful.

Now men rode to the horse-fight, and a very great crowd was gathered there. Gunnar was there and his brothers, and the sons of Sigfus. Njal and all his sons. There too was come Starkad and his sons, and Egil and his sons, and they said to Gunnar that now they would lead the horses together.

Gunnar said, "That is well."

Skarphedinn said: "Wilt thou that I drive thy horse, kinsman Gunnar?"

"I will not have that," said Gunnar.

"It wouldn't be amiss, though," says Skarphedinn; "we are hot-headed on both sides."

"Ye would say or do little," said Gunnar, "before a quarrel would spring up; but with me it will take longer, though it will be all the same in the end."

After that the horses were led together; Gunnar busked him to drive his horse, but Skarphedinn led him out. Gunnar was in a red kirtle, and had about his loins a broad belt, and a great riding-rod in his hand.

Then the horses ran at each other, and bit each other long, so that there was no need for anyone to touch them, and that was the greatest sport.

Then Thorgeir and Kol made up their minds that they would push their horse forward just as the horses rushed together, and see whether Gunnar would fall before him.

Now the horses ran at each other again, and both Thorgeir and Kol ran alongside their horse's flank.

Gunnar pushed his horse against them, and what happened in a trice was this, that Thorgeir and his brother fell down flat on their backs, and their horse a-top of them.

Then they sprang up and rushed at Gunnar. Gunnar swung himself free, seized Kol and cast him down on the field, so that he lay senseless. Thorgeir Starkad's son smote Gunnar's horse such a blow that one of his eyes started out. Gunnar smote Thorgeir with his riding-rod, and down fell Thorgeir senseless; but Gunnar went to his horse, and said to Kolskegg: "Cut off the horse's head; he shall not live a maimed and blemished beast."

So Kolskegg cut the head off the horse.

Then Thorgeir got on his feet and took his weapons, and attempted to fly at Gunnar, but that was stopped, and there was a great throng and crush.

Skarphedinn said, "This crowd wearies me, and it is far more manly that men should fight it out with weapons"; and so he sang a song—

> "At the Thing there is a throng;
> Past all bounds the crowding comes;
> Hard 'twill be to patch up peace
> 'Twixt the men: this wearies me;
> Worthier is it far for men
> Weapons red with gore to stain;
> I for one would sooner tame
> Hunger huge of cub of wolf."

Gunnar was still, so that one man held him, and spoke no ill words.

Njal tried to bring about a settlement, or to get pledges of peace; but Thorgeir said he would neither give nor take peace; far rather, he said, would he see Gunnar dead for the blow.

Kolskegg said: "Gunnar has before this stood too fast than that he should have fallen for words alone, and so it will be again."

Then men rode away from the horse-field, everyone to his home. They made no attack on Gunnar, and so that half-year passed away.

At the Thing the next summer Gunnar met Olaf the peacock, his cousin, and he asked him to come and see him, but bade him beware of himself: "For," said he, "they will do us all the harm they can, and mind and fare always with many men at thy back."

He gave him much good counsel besides and they agreed that there should be the greatest friendship between them.

the pilgrims the parents of whom her husband had spoken fondly, she refreshed them, and gave them change of raiment, dressing the mother in her own mantle, and, the more to honor them, she gave them her own sleeping quarters.

Julian returned at nightfall, and, as usual, seeking first his wife in her apartments, he came upon what, in his sudden astonishment and rage, seemed like proof of her infidelity, and without pause he smote the man and the woman. He had hardly struck the blow when the wail that rose overwhelmed him and he rushed in horror from the castle, when upon its steps he met Basilissa, returning from church. He started in amazement and could not trust his eyes. She drew him within, telling him she had a great pleasure in store for him; but he held her back and asked who were those persons in her bedchamber. "Your parents," she replied. He fell as if struck by lightning, and it was long before he recovered memory. When he did so, he confessed all and told her of the hart's prediction. "I must now say farewell to you, beloved of my heart," he added. "Pray for me, and forgive me, for I go to atone for my sin as best I may." "If you persist in leaving, I will be your companion, whithersoever you go," she answered, and they immediately set forth upon a pilgrimage. They continued their journey until they came to a little river called the Dender, where pilgrims on their way to the shrine of Our Lady of Hal had to cross at the risk of their lives, as there was no bridge. Julian formed the resolution to build a hut there, buy a boat, and by ferrying pilgrims obtain at last forgiveness for his sin. For seven years he ferried all who came, when one dark, rainy night, after a day of fatigue, as he lay on his bed of straw he heard a voice from the opposite bank calling to him and asking that he go and ferry a pilgrim who was suffering. Unheeding wind and weather, Julian turned his boat toward the other bank, and Basilissa knelt by his side and prayed, while the water raged so wildly that they were in great danger. They found an old pilgrim with dripping garments lying on the ground, groaning piteously, and they immediately covered him with their own mantles and carried him to the boat, which now seemed to steer toward the hut in tranquil water, though all beyond was in a tumult. When the shelter was reached they warmed and fed him, and suddenly they beheld a brilliant light diffuse itself as the pilgrim rose and stood in divine majesty and splendor. It was the Lord Jesus, and as Julian and Basilissa fell upon their knees before him, He said: "Thy sin is forgiven, Julian. I await thee and thy faithful wife," and He vanished from their sight.

The Kabouter Manneken.   During a great war the inhabitants of the village of Herselt were visited by multitudes of the little cave-folk. They ran back and forth to fetch and carry, but never seemed to harm anyone. When their women grew old they descended to one of the lowest caverns with a milk-loaf in their hands, and the cavern's mouth was then closed. Near the village of Gelrode the many hill-caverns were said to be habitations of Kabouter Manne-kens. If the miller's stone were worn, he had only to lay it outside his mill, together with a slice of bread and butter and a glass of beer, and he was sure of finding it next morning beautifully sharpened. And when he wanted his linen washed, the same, kind, mysterious hands did it up for him. One race of these dwarfs was called Red-caps, or Klabbers, and their special favor was to increase the wood-pile. In the night when the moon does not shine they enter a house through the chimney, build a hearth-fire and sit quietly before it. No one can see the fire except the Redcaps, though it gives out more heat than an ordinary fire. In the morning the housewife often finds of her large bundle of brushwood only a few twigs, but she cheerfully lights these because she knows they will double the warmth of those in the bundle. If the woman should forget her-self and make a sign of the cross, or curse a Redcap, the blaze would go out instantly.

A poor peasant whose wife had been taken ill in the night rose to do the churning, having placed everything in readiness the eve-ning before, and set the milk in large pots near the fire. On entering the room he found, to his amazement, that the fire was burning and a little man was half asleep before it. The noise of the peasant's wooden shoes waked him, and he started up and looked hard at him, without speaking. The peasant was equally silent, but he saw, by a side glance, that the little intruder was dressed in red from head to foot, and that his face and hands were green. Then, looking straight before him, he brought the bundle of firewood and then lay down to sleep. Next morning the butter was all set and ready, so that he had only to take it to market; and there was, moreover, a larger quantity than he had ever gotten from the milk. His wife recovered, Redcap continued to churn for them, and the man grad-

and then they asked for a guide to take them back to their parents.

The host then arose and said: "Dear friends, now that Malegy's Palfrey has procured us the pleasure of receiving in our mansion these noble damsels from Ypres, we must neglect nothing that will contribute to their pleasure. Let us play at forfeits." The ladies had already ranged themselves in a circle, leaving places vacant for the guests, but Magdalena said: "I cannot play with you. My parents will be greatly alarmed if I stay longer." "Nor can I," said Lucia. "Nor I," said Maxima. At this refusal the eyes of the master assumed such a diabolical expression that in fright they quickly sat down in the circle so as not to behold it. They then played at forfeits, and when it came their turns to repeat the formula after the master they were so disconcerted by his looks that they lost every time. They played until they had forfeited their earrings, finger-rings, chains, bracelets, and even their garments. "Now," said the leader, "before we redeem the forfeits, let us drink to the health of Malegy's Palfrey, which has so wondrously brought the young ladies to our dwelling." They lifted the glasses to their lips as the master uttered some mysterious words; but no sooner had they drunk than they found themselves, as if waking from a dream, under the open sky in the hollow of a pit. The sorcery was at an end. Half-naked, barefooted and bareheaded, they slowly made their way by the light of the stars above them, which seemed to proclaim midnight. At last they discerned a faint shining in the distance, and following its course, they arrived at a peasant's cottage. In response to their knocking the man asked what they wanted, and they told of their plight, and asked where they were. Their dejection can be imagined when they learned that they were many miles from Ypres, and had been in a cave of the Kimmelberg at midnight. They asked for clothes and a guide home, but the woman said: "No klaes, give them no help; persons who dare to appear naked at our door can be no other than sorceresses come to bewitch our child. I hear it crying already." "Only an hour ago," said the man, "I put my head out of the window and the witches that live in the mountain were making a hideous noise. I saw naught but a great light, but I heard music and dancing." "If you have been with them," called out the woman, "I'd rather burn you than give you klaes." "You're right, wife," said the man. "It is impossible that three young maids from Ypres, daughters of respectable folk, should be in the Kimmelberg at such an hour without clothes."

The maidens came at last to a hostelry, at the door of which they knocked, but they dared not repeat their story to the master lest they should receive the same treatment, and they invented a tale of robbery, at which they were welcomed and received garments. When Magdalena told him that she was the daughter of Baldwin Ghyselin, the host exclaimed: "That being the case, I will instantly put the horses to my wagon and carry you home." When they had ridden about an hour it appeared to the host that he must have taken the wrong road. "I know the way from Kimmel to Ypres as well as I know my Paternoster," said he, "and yet I am far off the track, and, what is strange, I cannot govern the horses. Here we are now in the middle of a field, and I cannot imagine how the horses could have dragged the wagon into it." As he spoke, the wagon was dragged with violence over dikes, through thickets, over plowed land, and through streams. A shadow floated ever before them. "The shadow of the palfrey," whispered the girls, shuddering. At last they entered a broad road, and the horses stopped, reeking with sweat. The shadow vanished, and the day began to dawn. "The witches of the Kimmelberg have misled us," said the host, pale as a ghost, "but their power is at an end. Yonder is the sunrise." "Where am I, friend?" asked the host of a countryman. "I know the road from Kimmel to Ypres blindfolded, but I have lost my way this time." "I believe you," was the answer. "You talk of Ypres, and you are a good ten hours' distance from it on the road from Steenvorde to Cassel." It was nightfall once more before the girls were placed in the arms of their wondering and distracted parents.

The Poacher of Wetteren-Overbeke. At Wetteren-Overbeke there was once a poacher who had been out all day but had shot nothing. His ill-luck made him feel so obstinate that he resolved to remain in the field in the hope of meeting some game, and not being obliged to return home with an empty pouch. It was just midnight when, by the moonlight, he saw a hare frisking about in the clover. He aimed at the animal and fired, but the recoil of the gun was so strong as to knock him down, and on rising and examining the fowling-piece he found it to be very crooked. This was unaccountable, as the load it had contained was no heavier than usual. At the same instant the animal that he supposed himself to have killed, started up and came toward him, but, as he came, he was transformed from a hare to a black ball slowly rolling along. The poor poacher took to his heels, fully convinced that it was no other than the devil himself that was chasing him. The ball continued to follow him, rolling, and grew bigger and bigger. At last, with sweat pouring from him, the terrified man succeeded in climbing a tree, where he hoped to find safety, but the black ball came rolling up the tree, and was now become so large as to darken the landscape. Terror seized the poacher, and, falling on his knees as he clung to the limb, he confessed his sins and vowed never to poach again, when the black ball slid down and disappeared.

The Sand-Gate at Mechlin. A terrific storm is thus preserved in legend in Mechlin. The sand-gate of the city was once used for a magazine, and during the storm lightning struck the sand-gate and tore the tower into a thousand fragments, while hundreds of buildings were likewise destroyed by the shock. The city's ditches were dried up, and the fishes were found either boiled or roasted. More than four hundred persons were killed and as many more were wounded. The sacristans of Mechlin and the surrounding towns rang the bells in the church towers during all the storm. Later, some merchants reported that at the very hour that the sand-gate was struck they were in a mill in Friesland when they saw devils in the air conducting their flight toward Mechlin. One of them called to his companion, "Krombeen (crooked-leg), take the mill with you." "I can't, I can't; I must hasten to Mechlin. Kortstaert (short-tail) is behind us; the mill is left for him." "And, in fact," the merchants added, "the mill was struck down the same night." The sacristan of Putte tried to ring the bell of his church, but he could not get into the building. "Surely," said he, "there must be more than one devil at work here." "No, there you are wrong," said a mocking voice near by. "The others are off to Mechlin."

Zevenbergen, the Hidden City. On the road to Dort may be seen a lonely tower which rises out of the middle of a large body of water. There once stood the populous city of Zevenbergen, the inhabitants of which used gold and silver as if they had been copper. All the latches of their doors and the hasps of their windows were of pure gold; all the nails in the houses and all the cooking-utensils were of pure silver. Indeed, their riches baffle description, and so does their consequent arrogance. But it finally happened that every night a mermaid came flying and seated herself on the tower of the church and sang. The church had been dedicated to St. Lobbetjen, and the words she sang were:

> "Zevenbergen shall perish,
> And Lobbetjen's tower remain standing."

Everybody heard the song, but nobody heeded it. At last, as it is said, the patience of the Almighty was wearied with the arrogance of the people, and so terrible a storm of wind and rain and lightning arose that the city perished in an hour and nothing remained standing except the tower of the church. A great expanse of water covered the site, and even now the fishermen, as they float over that lake, can look far down in the clear water and see the glittering, gilded roofs of Zevenbergen, but no one has descended to those mysterious depths.

PART VII.

ANGLO-SAXON MYTHOLOGY

Arthur and **Guenever.** In the beginning of Arthur, after he was chosen King, by adventure and by grace—for the most part of the barons knew not that he was Uther Pendragon's son, but as Merlin made it openly known—many kings and lords made great war against him for that cause; but well Arthur overcame them all; for the most part of the days of his life he was ruled much by the counsel of Merlin. So it fell on a time King Arthur said unto Merlin:

"My barons will let me have no rest, but needs I must take a wife, and I will none take but by thy counsel and by thine advice."

"It is well done," said Merlin, "that ye take a wife, for a man of your bounty and nobleness should not be without a wife. Now is there any that ye love more than another?"

"Yea," said King Arthur, "I love Guenever, the daughter of King Leodegrance, of the land of Cameliard, which Leodegrance holdeth in his house the Table Round, that ye told he had of my father, Uther. And this damsel is the most valiant and fairest lady that I know living, or yet that ever I could find."

"Sir," said Merlin, "as of her beauty and fairness she is one of the fairest on live. But and ye loved her not so well as ye do, I could find you a damsel of beauty and of goodness that should like you and please you, and your heart were not set; but there as a man's heart is set, he will be loath to return."

"That is truth," said King Arthur.

But Merlin warned the King covertly that Guenever was not wholesome for him to take to wife, for he warned him that Launcelot should love her, and she him again; and so he turned his tale to the adventures of the Sangreal. Then Merlin desired of the King to have men with him that should inquire of Guenever, and so the King granted him. And Merlin went forth to King Leodegrance of Cameliard, and told him of the desire of the King that he would have unto his wife Guenever, his daughter.

"That is to me," said King Leodegrance, "the best tidings that ever I heard, that so worthy a king of prowess and noblesse will wed my daughter. And as for my lands I will give him wist I it might please him, but he hath lands enough, him needeth none, but I shall send him a gift shall please him much more, for I shall give him the Table Round, the which Uther Pendragon gave me, and when it is full complete there is an hundred knights and fifty. And as for an hundred good knights I have myself, but I lack fifty, for so many have been slain in my days."

And so King Leodegrance delivered his daughter Guenever unto Merlin, and the Table Round, with the hundred knights, and so they rode freshly, with great royalty, what by water and what by land, till that they came nigh unto London.

When King Arthur heard of the coming of Guenever and the hundred knights with the Table Round, then King Arthur made great joy for their coming, and that rich present, and said openly:

"This fair lady is passing welcome unto me, for I have loved her long, and therefore there is nothing so lief to me. And these knights with the Round Table please me more than right great riches."

And in all haste the King let ordain for the marriage and the coronation in the most honorablest wise that could be devised.

"Now, Merlin," said King Arthur, "go thou and espy me in all this land fifty knights which be of most prowess and worship."

Within short time Merlin had found such knights that should fulfil twenty and eight knights, but no more he could find. Then the Bishop of Canterbury was fetched, and he blessed the sieges with great royalty and devotion, and there set the eight and twenty knights in their sieges. And when this was done Merlin said:

"Fair sirs, ye must all arise and come to King Arthur for to do him homage; he will have the better will to maintain you."

And so they arose and did their homage. And when they were gone Merlin found in every siege letters of gold that told the knights' names that had sitten therein. But two sieges were void. And so anon came young Gawaine, and asked the King a gift.

"Ask," said the King, "and I shall grant it you."

"Sir, I ask that ye will make me knight that same day ye shall wed fair Guenever."

"I will do it with a good will," said King Arthur, "and do unto you all the worship that I may, for I must by reason you are my nephew, my sister's son."

Forthwithal there came a poor man into the court, and brought with him a fair young man of eighteen year of age, riding upon a lean mare. And the poor man asked all men that he met:

"Where shall I find King Arthur?"

"Yonder he is," said the knights; "wilt thou anything with him?"

"Yea," said the poor man, "therefore I came hither."

Anon as he came before the King, he saluted him and said:

"O King Arthur, the flower of all knights and kings, I beseech Jesu save thee. Sir, it was told me that at this time of your marriage ye would give any man the gift that he would ask out, except that were unreasonable."

"That is truth," said the King; "such cries I let make, and that will I hold, so it impair not my realm nor mine estate."

"Ye say well and graciously," said the poor man. "Sir, I ask nothing else but that ye will make my son here a knight."

"It is a great thing that thou askest of me: what is thy name?" said the King to the poor man.

"Sir, my name is Aries the cowherd."

"Whether cometh this of thee or of thy son?" said the King.

"Nay, sir," said Aries, "this desire cometh of my son, and not of me. For I shall tell you I have thirteen sons, and all they will fall to what labor I put them to, and will be right glad to do labor, but this child will do no labor for me, for anything that my wife or I may do, but always he will be shooting or casting darts, and glad for to see battles, and to behold knights; and always day and night he desireth of me to be made a knight."

"What is thy name?" said the King unto the young man.

"Sir, my name is Tor."

The King beheld him fast, and saw he was passingly well visaged and passingly well made of his years.

"Well," said King Arthur to Aries the cowherd, "fetch all thy sons afore me, that I may see them."

And so the poor man did, and all were shapen much like the poor man; but Tor was not like none of them all in shape nor in countenance, for he was much more than any of them.

"Now," said King Arthur unto the cowherd, "where is the sword that he shall be made knight withal?"

"It is here," said Tor.

"Take it out of the sheath," said the King, "and require me to make you a knight."

Then Tor alight off his mare, and pulled out his sword, kneeling, and requiring the King that he would make him knight, and that he might be a knight of the Table Round.

"As for a knight, I will make you;" and therewith smote him in the neck with the sword, saying: "Be ye a good knight, and so I pray to God so ye may be, and if ye be of prowess and of worthiness ye shall be a knight of the Table Round.   Now, Merlin," said Arthur, "say whether this Tor shall be a good knight or no."

"Yea, sir, he ought to be a good knight, for he is come of as good a man as any is on live, and of king's blood."

"How so, sir?" said the King.

"I shall tell you," said Merlin.   "This poor man, Aries the cowherd, is not his father, he is nothing like to him, for King Pellinore is his father."

"I suppose nay," said the cowherd.

"Fetch thy wife afore me," said Merlin, "and she shall not say nay."

Anon the wife was fetched, which was a fair housewife, and there she answered Merlin full womanly.   And there she told the King and Merlin that when she was a maid, and went to milk kine, "There met with me a stern knight, and half by force he held me, and after that time was born my son Tor, and he took away from me my greyhound that I had that time with me, and said that he would keep the greyhound for my love."

"Ah," said the cowherd, "I wend not this, but I may believe it well, for he had never no taches of me."

"Sir," said Tor to Merlin, "dishonor not my mother."

"Sir," said Merlin, "it is more for your worship than hurt, for your father is a good man and a King, and he may right well advance you and your mother, for ye were begotten or ever she was wedded."

"That is truth," said the wife.

"It is the less grief to me," said the cowherd.

So on the morn King Pellinore came to the court of King Arthur, which had great joy of him, and told him of Tor, how he was his son, and how he had made him knight at the request of the cowherd. When King Pellinore beheld Tor he pleased him much. So the King made Gawaine knight, but Tor was the first he made at the feast.

"What is the cause," said King Arthur, "that there be two places void in the sieges?"

"Sir," said Merlin, "there shall no man sit in those places, but they that shall be of most worship. But in the Siege Perilous there shall no man sit therein but one, and if there be any so hardy to do it he shall be destroyed, and he that shall sit there shall have no fellow."

And therewith Merlin took King Pellinore by the hand, and in the one hand next the two sieges and the Siege Perilous he said, in open audience:

"This is your place, and best ye are worthy to sit therein of any that is here."

Thereat sat Sir Gawaine in great envy, and told Gaheris his brother:

"Yonder knight is put to great worship, the which grieveth me sore, for he slew our father, King Lot; therefore I will slay him," said Gawaine, "with a sword that was sent me that is passing trenchant."

"Ye shall not so," said Gaheris, "at this time; for at this time I am but a squire, and when I am made knight I will be avenged on him; and therefore, brother, it is best ye suffer till another time, that we may have him out of the court, for and we did so we should trouble this high feast."

"I will well," said Gawaine, "as ye will."

Then was the high feast made ready, and the King was wedded at Camelot unto Dame Guenever in the Church of St. Stephen's, with great solemnity. And as every man was set after his degree, Merlin went to all the knights of the Round Table, and bad them sit still, that none of them remove, "For ye shall see a strange and a marvelous adventure."

Right so as they sat there came running in a white hart into the hall, and a white brachet next him, and thirty couple of black running hounds came after with a great cry, and the hart went about the Table Round. As he went by other boards, the white brachet bit him by the haunch and pulled out a piece, where through the hart leapt a great leap and overthrew a knight that sat at the board side, and therewith the knight arose and took up the brachet, and so went forth out of the hall, and took his horse and rode his way with the brachet. Right so anon came in a lady on a white palfrey, and cried aloud to King Arthur:

"Sir, suffer me not to have this despite, for the brachet was mine that the knight led away."

"I may not do therewith," said the King.

With this there came a knight riding all armed on a great horse, and took the lady away with him with force, and ever she cried and made a great dole. When she was gone, the King was glad, for she made such a noise.

"Nay," said Merlin, "ye may not leave these adventures so lightly, for these adventures must be brought again or else it would be disworship to you and to your feast."

"I will," said the King, "that all be done by your advice."

"Then," said Merlin, "let call Sir Gawaine, for he must bring again the white hart. Also, sir, ye must let call Sir Tor, for he must bring again the brachet and the knight, or else slay him. Also let call King Pellinore, for he must bring again the lady and the knight, or else slay him. And these three knights shall do marvelous adventures or they come again."

Then were they called all three as it rehearseth afore, and every each of them took his charge, and armed them surely. But Sir Gawaine had the first request, and therefore we will begin at him.

Sir Gawaine rode more than a pace, and Gaheris his brother rode with him, instead of a squire, to do him service. So as they rode they saw two knights fight on horseback passing sore, so Sir Gawaine and his brother rode 'twixt them, and asked them for what cause they fought so. The one knight answered and said:

"We fight for a simple matter, for we two be two brethren, born and begotten of one man and of one woman."

"Alas!" said Sir Gawaine, "why do ye so?"

"Sir," said the elder, "there came a white hart this way this day, and many hounds chased him, and a white brachet was alway next him, and we understood it was adventure made for the high feast of King Arthur, and therefore I would have gone after to have won me worship; and here my younger brother said he would go after the hart, for he was a better knight than I; and for this cause we fell at debate, and so we thought to prove which of us both was better knight."

"This is a simple cause," said Sir Gawaine; "strange men should debate withal, and not brother with brother; therefore but if ye will do by my counsel I will have ado with you—that is, ye shall yield you unto me, and that ye go unto King Arthur and yield you unto his grace."

"Sir knight," said the two brethren, "we are for-foughten, and much blood have we lost through our wilfulness, and therefore we would be loth to have ado with you."

"Then do as I will have you," said Sir Gawaine.

"We will agree to fulfil your will; but by whom shall we say that we be thither sent?"

"Ye may say, by the knight that followeth the quest of the hart that was white. Now what is your name?" said Sir Gawaine.

"Sorlouse of the Forest," said the elder.

"And my name is," said the younger, "Brian of the Forest."

And so they departed and went to the King's court, and Sir Gawaine on his quest. And as Sir Gawaine followed the hart by the cry of the hounds, even afore him there was a great river, and the hart swam over; and as Sir Gawaine would follow after there stood a knight over the other side, and said:

"Sir knight, come not over after this hart, but if thou wilt just with me."

"I will not fail as for that," said Sir Gawaine, "to follow the quest that I am in," and so made his horse to swim over the water, and anon they gat their spears and ran together full hard, but Sir Gawaine smote him off his horse, and then he turned his horse and bad him yield him.

"Nay," said the knight, "not so, though thou have the better of me on horseback. I pray thee, valiant knight, alight afoot, and match we together with swords."

"What is your name?" said Sir Gawaine.

"Allardin of the Isles," said the other.

Then either dressed their shields and smote together, but Sir Gawaine smote him so hard through the helm that it went to the brains, and the knight fell down dead.

"Ah!" said Gaheris, "that was a mighty stroke of a young knight."

Then Gawaine and Gaheris rode more than a pace after the white hart, and let slip at the hart three couple of greyhounds, and so they chased the hart into a castle, and in the chief place of the castle they slew the hart. Sir Gawaine and Gaheris followed after. Right so there came a knight out of a chamber with a sword drawn in his hand and slew two of the greyhounds, even in the sight of Sir Gawaine, and the remnant he chased them with his sword out of the castle. And when he came again, he said:

"O my white hart, me repenteth that thou art dead, for my sovereign lady gave thee to me, and evil have I kept thee, and thy death shall be dear bought and I live."

And anon he went into his chamber and armed him, and came out fiercely, and there met he with Sir Gawaine.

"Why have ye slain my hounds?" said Sir Gawaine, "for they did but their kind, and lever I had ye had wroken your anger upon me than upon a dumb beast."

"Thou sayest truth," said the knight; "I have avenged me on thy hounds, and so I will on thee or thou go."

Then Sir Gawaine alight afoot, and dressed his shield, and they stroke together mightily, and clave their shields, and stoned their helms, and brake their hauberks that the blood ran down to their feet. At the last Sir Gawaine smote the knight so hard that he fell to the earth; and then he cried mercy and yielded him, and besought him as he was a knight and gentleman to save his life.

"Thou shalt die," said Gawaine, "for slaying of my hounds."

"I will make amends," said the knight, "unto my power."

Sir Gawaine would no mercy have, but unlaced his helm to have stricken off his head; right so came his lady out of a chamber and fell over him, and so he smote off her head by misadventure.

"Alas!" said Gaheris, "that is foul and shamefully done; that shame shall never from you. Also, ye should give mercy unto them that ask mercy; for a knight without mercy is without worship."

Sir Gawaine was so astonished at the death of this fair lady that he wist not what he did, and said unto the knight, "Arise, I will give thee mercy."

"Nay, nay," said the knight, "I care for no mercy now, for thou hast slain my love and my lady that I loved best of all earthly things."

"Me repenteth it," said Sir Gawaine, "for I thought to strike unto thee. But now thou shalt go unto King Arthur, and tell him of

Tor espied that the other knight fainted, and then he sued fast upon him, and doubled his strokes, and made him go to the earth on the one side. Then Sir Tor bad him yield him.

"That will I not," said Abelleus, "while my life lasteth and the soul is within my body, unless that thou wilt give me the brachet."

"That will I not do," said Sir Tor, "for it was my quest to bring again thy brachet, thee, or both."

With that came a damsel riding on a palfrey as fast as she might drive and cried with a loud voice unto Sir Tor.

"What will ye with me?" said Sir Tor.

"I beseech thee," said the damsel, "for King Arthur's love, give me a gift; I require thee, gentle knight, as thou art a gentleman."

"Now," said Sir Tor, "ask a gift, and I will give it you."

"Gramercy," said the damsel. "Now I ask the head of the false knight Abelleus, for he is the most outrageous knight that liveth, and the greatest murderer."

"I am loth," said Sir Tor, "of that gift I have given you; let him make amends in that he hath trespassed unto you."

"Now," said the damsel, "he may not, for he slew mine own brother afore mine own eyes, that was a better knight than he, and he had had grace; and I kneeled half an hour afore him in the mire for to save my brother's life, that had done him no damage, but fought with him by adventure of arms, and so for all that I could do he struck off his head; wherefore, I require thee, as thou art a true knight, to give me my gift, or else I shall shame thee in all the court of King Arthur; for he is the falsest knight living, and a great destroyer of good knights."

Then when Abelleus heard this, he was more afeard, and yielded him and asked mercy.

"I may not now," said Sir Tor, "but if I should be found false of my promise, for while I would have taken you to mercy ye would none ask, but if ye had the brachet again that was my quest."

And therewith he took off his helm, and he arose and fled, and Sir Tor after him, and smote off his head quite.

"Now, sir," said the damsel, "it is near night; I pray you come and lodge with me here at my place; it is here fast by."

"I will well," said Sir Tor; for his horse and he had fared evil since they departed from Camelot, and so he rode with her, and had passing good cheer with her; and she had a passing fair old knight to her husband that made him passing good cheer, and well eased both his horse and him. And on the morn he heard his mass, and brake his fast, and took his leave of the knight and of the lady, that besought him to tell them his name.

"Truly," he said, "my name is Sir Tor, that late was made knight, and this was the first quest of arms that ever I did, to bring again that this knight Abelleus took away from King Arthur's court."

"O fair knight," said the lady and her husband, "and ye come here in our marches, come and see our poor lodging, and it shall be always at your commandment."

So Sir Tor departed, and came to Camelot on the third day by noon. And the King and the Queen and all the court was passing fain of his coming, and made great joy that he was come again; for he went from the court with little succor, but as King Pellinore his father gave him an old courser, and King Arthur gave him armor and a sword, and else had he none other succor, but rode so forth himself alone. And then the King and the Queen by Merlin's advice made him to swear to tell of his adventures, and so he told and made proofs of his deeds as it is afore rehearsed, wherefore the King and the Queen made great joy.

"Nay, nay," said Merlin, "these be but jests to that he shall do; he shall prove a noble knight of prowess, as good as any is living, and gentle and courteous, and of good parts, and passing true of his promise, and never shall outrage."

Where through Merlin's words King Arthur gave him an earldom of lands that fell unto him. And here endeth the quest of Sir Tor, King Pellinore's son.

Then King Pellinore armed him and mounted upon his horse, and rode more than a pace after the lady that the knight led away. And as he rode in a forest, he saw in a valley a damsel sit by a well, and a wounded knight in her arms, and Pellinore saluted her. And when she was ware of him, she cried over-loud:

"Help me, knight, for Christ's sake, King Pellinore!"

And he would not tarry, he was so eager in his quest, and ever she cried an hundred times after help. When she saw he would not abide, she prayed unto God to send him as much need of help as she had, and that he might feel it or he died. So as the book telleth, the knight died that there was wounded, wherefore the lady for pure sorrow slew herself with his sword. As King Pellinore rode in that valley he met with a poor man, a laborer:

"Sawest thou not," said Pellinore, "a knight riding and leading away a lady?"

"Yea," said the poor man, "I saw that knight, and the lady that made great dole. And yonder beneath in a valley there shall ye see two pavilions, and one of the knights of the pavilions challenged that lady of that knight, and said she was his cousin near, wherefore he should lead her no farther. And so they waged battle in that quarrel; the one said he would have her by force, and the other said he would have the rule of her because he was her kinsman, and would lead her to her kin. For this quarrel I left them fighting, and if ye will ride a pace ye shall find them fighting, and the lady was beleft with the two squires in the pavilions."

"I thank thee," said King Pellinore.

Then he rode a wallop till that he had a sight of the two pavilions and the two knights fighting. Anon he rode unto the pavilions, and saw the lady that was his quest, and said:

"Fair lady, ye must go with me unto the court of King Arthur."

"Sir knight," said the two squires that were with her, "yonder are two knights that fight for this lady, go thither and depart them, and be agreed with them, and then ye may have her at your pleasure."

"Ye say well," said King Pellinore.

And anon he rode betwixt them, and departed them, and asked them the cause why that they fought.

"Sir knight," said the one, "I shall tell you. This lady is my kinswoman nigh, mine aunt's daughter, and when I heard her complain that she was with him maugre her head, I waged battle to fight with him."

"Sir knight," said the other, whose name was Hontzlake of Wentland, "and this lady I gat by my prowess of arms this day at Arthur's court."

"That is untruly said," said King Pellinore, "for ye came in suddenly there as we were at the high feast, and took away this lady or any man might him ready, and therefore it was my quest for to bring her again and you both, or else the one of us to abide in the field; therefore the lady shall go with me, or I will die for it, for I have promised it King Arthur. And therefore fight ye no more, for none of you shall have no part of her at this time, and if ye list to fight for her, fight with me, and I will defend her."

"Well," said the knights, "make you ready, and we shall assail you with all our power."

And as King Pellinore would have put his horse from them, Sir Hontzlake rove his horse through with a sword, and said:

"Now art thou on foot as well we are."

When King Pellinore espied that his horse was slain, lightly he leapt from his horse and pulled out his sword, and put his shield afore him, and said:

"Knight, keep well thy head, for thou shalt have a buffet for the slaying of my horse."

So King Pellinore gave him such a stroke upon the helm that he clave the head down to the chin, that he fell to the earth dead.

And then he turned him to the other knight that was sore wounded. But when he saw the other's buffet he would not fight, but kneeled down and said:

"Take my cousin, the lady, with you at your request, and I require you, as ye be a true knight, put her to no shame nor villainy."

"What," said King Pellinore, "will ye not fight for her?"

"No, sir," said the knight, "I will not fight with such a knight of prowess as ye be."

"Well," said Pellinore, "ye say well, I promise you she shall have no villainy by me, as I am true knight; but now me lacketh an horse," said Pellinore, "but I will have Hontzlake's horse."

"Ye shall not need," said the knight, "for I shall give you such a horse as shall please you, so that ye will lodge with me, for it is near night."

"I will well," said King Pellinore, "abide with you all night."

And there he had with him right good cheer, and fared of the best with passing good wine, and had merry rest that night. And on the morrow he heard a mass, and dined: and then was brought him a fair bay courser, and King Pellinore's saddle set upon him.

"Now, what shall I call you?" said the knight, "inasmuch as ye have my cousin at your desire of your quest."

"Sir, I shall tell you, my name is King Pellinore of the Isles, and knight of the Table Round."

"Now I am glad," said the knight, "that such a noble man shall have the rule of my cousin."

"What is now your name?" said Pellinore, "I pray you tell me."

"Sir, my name is Sir Meliot of Logurs, and this lady my cousin, hight Nimue, and the knight that was in the other pavilion is my sworn brother, a passing good knight, and his name is Brian of the Isles, and he is full loth to do wrong, and full loth to fight with any man, but if he be sore sought on, so that for shame he may not leave it."

"It is marvel," said Pellinore, "that he will not have ado with me."

"Sir, he will not have ado with no man but if it be at his request."

"Bring him to the court," said Pellinore, "one of these days."

"Sir, we will come together."

"And ye shall be welcome," said King Pellinore, "to the court of King Arthur, and greatly allowed for your coming."

And so he departed with the lady, and brought her to Camelot. So as they rode in a valley it was full of stones, and there the lady's horse stumbled and threw her down, wherewith her arm was sore bruised, and near she swooned for pain.

"Alas! sir," said the lady, "mine arm is out of joint, where through I must needs rest me."

"Ye shall well," said King Pellinore.

And so he alighted under a fair tree where was fair grass, and he put his horse thereto, and so laid him under the tree and slept till it was nigh night. And when he awoke he would have ridden.

"Sir," said the lady, "it is so dark that ye may as well ride backward as forward."

So they abode still and made there their lodging. Then Sir Pellinore put off his armor; then a little afore midnight they heard the trotting of an horse.

"Be ye still," said King Pellinore, "for we shall hear of some adventure."

And therewith he armed him. So right even afore him there met two knights; the one came from Camelot and the other from the north, and either saluted other.

"What tidings at Camelot?" said the one.

"By my head," said the other, "there have I been, and espied the court of King Arthur, and there is such a fellowship they may never be broken, and well-nigh all the world holdeth with Arthur, for there is the flower of chivalry. Now for this cause I am riding into the north to tell our chieftains of the fellowship that is withholden with King Arthur."

"As for that," said the other knight, "I have brought a remedy with me, that is the greatest poison that ever ye heard speak of, and to Camelot will I with it, for we have a friend right nigh King Arthur, and well cherished, that shall poison King Arthur, for so he hath promised our chieftains, and received great gifts for to do it."

"Beware," said the other knight, "of Merlin, for he knoweth all things by the devil's craft."

"Therefore will I not let it," said the knight.

And so they departed in sunder. Anon after Pellinore made him ready, and his lady, and rode toward Camelot. And as they came by the well there as the wounded knight was and the lady, there he found the knight, and the lady eaten with lions or wild beasts all save the head, wherefore he made great sorrow, and wept passing sore, and said:

"Alas, her life might I have saved, but I was so fierce in my quest therefore I would not abide."

"Wherefore make ye such dole?" said the lady.

"I wot not," said Pellinore, "but my heart mourneth sore for the death of her, for she was a passing fair lady and a young."

"Now will ye do by mine advice," said the lady, "take this knight and let him be buried in an hermitage, and then take the lady's head and bear it with you unto Arthur."

So King Pellinore took this dead knight on his shoulders and brought him to the hermitage, and charged the hermit with the corpse, that service should be done for the soul.

"And take his harness for your pain."

"It shall be done," said the hermit, "as I will answer unto God."

And therewith they departed and came there as the head of the lady lay with a fair yellow hair, that grieved King Pellinore passingly sore when he looked on it, for much he cast his heart on the visage. And so by noon they came to Camelot. And the King and the Queen were passing fain of his coming to the court. And there he was made to swear upon the four Evangelists to tell the truth of his quest from the one to the other.

"Ah, Sir Pellinore," said Queen Guenever, "ye were greatly to blame that ye saved not this lady's life."

"Madam," said Pellinore, "ye were greatly to blame and ye would not save your own life and ye might; but saving your pleasure, I was so furious in my quest that I would not abide, and that repenteth me, and shall the days of my life."

"Truly," said Merlin, "ye ought sore to repent it, for the lady was your own daughter, and that knight that was dead was her love, and should have wedded her, and he was a right good knight of a young man, and would have proved a good man, and to this court was he coming, and his name was Sir Miles of the lands, and a knight came behind him and slew him with a spear, and his name is Loraine le Savage, a false knight and a coward; and she for great sorrow and dole slew herself with his sword, and her name was Eleine. And because ye would not abide and help her, ye shall see your best friend fail you when ye be in the greatest distress that ever ye were or shall be. And that penance God hath ordained you for that deed, that he that ye shall most trust to of any man alive, he shall leave you there as ye shall be slain."

"Me forthinketh," said King Pellinore, "that this shall betide, but God may well fordo destiny."

Thus when the quest was done of the white hart, the which followed Sir Gawaine; and the quest of the brachet followed of Sir Tor, Pellinore's son; and the quest of the lady that the knight took away, the which King Pellinore at that time followed; then the King stablished all his knights, and them that were of lands not rich he gave them lands, and charged them never to do outrage, nor murder, and always to flee treason. Also, by no mean to be cruel, but to give mercy unto him that asketh mercy, upon pain of forfeiture of their worship and lordship of King Arthur forevermore; and always to do ladies, damsels, and gentlewomen succor upon pain of death. Also, that no man take no battles in a wrongful quarrel for no law, nor for world's goods. Unto this were all the knights sworn of the Round Table, both old and young. And every year were they sworn at the high feast of Pentecost.

Launcelot's Adventures. Soon after that King Arthur was come from Rome into England, then all the knights of the Table Round resorted unto the King, and made many justs and tournaments; and some there were that were but knights which increased so in arms and worship that they passed all their fellows in prowess and noble deeds, and that was well proved on many. But in especial it was proved on Sir Launcelot du Lake; for in all tournaments

and justs and deeds of arms, both for life and death, he passed all
other knights, and at no time he was never overcome but if it were
by treason or enchantment. So Sir Launcelot increased so marvelously in worship and honor. Wherefore Queen Guenever had
him in great favor above all other knights, and in certain he loved
the Queen ᆺ gain above all other ladies and damsels all his life, and
for her he did many deeds of arms and saved her from the fire through
his noble chivalry. Thus Sir Launcelot rested him long with play
and game. And then he thought himself to prove himself in strange
adventures: then he bade his nephew Sir Lionel for to make him
ready, "for we two will seek adventures." So they mounted on their
horses, armed at all rights, and rode into a deep forest, and so into
a deep plain. And then the weather was hot about noon, and Sir
Launcelot had great lust to sleep. Then Sir Lionel espied a great
apple-tree that stood by an hedge, and said:

"Brother, yonder is a fair shadow; there may we rest us and our
horses."

"It is well said, fair brother," said Sir Launcelot, "for this seven
year I was not so sleepy as I am now."

And so they there alighted, and tied their horses unto sundry trees,
and so Sir Launcelot laid him down under an apple-tree, and his
helm he laid under his head. And Sir Lionel waked while he slept.
So Sir Launcelot was asleep passing fast. And in the meanwhile there
came three knights riding, as fast fleeing as ever they might ride.
And there followed them three but one knight. And when Sir Lionel
saw him, him thought he saw never so great a knight nor so well
faring a man, neither so well appareled unto all rights. So within
a while this strong knight had overtaken one of these knights, and
there he smote him to the cold earth that he lay still. And then he
rode unto the second knight, and smote him so that man and horse
fell down. And then straight to the third knight he rode, and he
smote him behind his horse tail a spear's length. And then he alight
down, and reined his horse on the bridle, and bound all the three
knights fast with the reins of their own bridles. When Sir Lionel
saw him do thus, he thought to assay him, and made him ready,
and stilly and privily he took his horse, and thought not for to awake
Sir Launcelot. And when he was mounted upon his horse he overtook this strong knight and bad him turn: and the other smote Sir
Lionel so hard that horse and man he bare to the earth, and so he

alight down and bound him fast, and threw him overthwart his own horse, and so he served them all four, and rode with them away to his own castle. And when he came there, he made unarm them, and beat them with thorns all naked, and after put them in a deep prison where there were many more knights that made great dolor.

When Sir Ector de Maris wist that Sir Launcelot was past out of the court to seek adventures he was wroth with himself and made him ready to seek Sir Launcelot, and as he had ridden long in a great forest, he met with a man that was like a forester.

"Fair fellow," said Sir Ector, "knowest thou in this country any adventures that be here nigh hand?"

"Sir," said the forester, "this country know I well, and hereby within this mile is a strong manor, and well diked, and by that manor, on the left hand, there is a fair ford for horses to drink of, and over that ford there groweth a fair tree, and thereon hangeth many fair shields that wielded sometime good knights: and at the hole of the tree hangeth a bason of copper and laton, and strike upon that bason with the butt of thy spear thrice, and soon after thou shalt hear new tidings, and else hast thou the fairest grace that many a year had ever knight that passed through this forest."

"Gramercy," said Sir Ector, and departed and came to the tree, and saw many fair shields, and among them he saw his brother's shield, Sir Lionel, and many more that he knew that were his fellows of the Round Table, the which grieved his heart, and he promised to revenge his brother. Then anon Sir Ector beat on the bason as he were wood, and then he gave his horse drink at the ford: and there came a knight behind him and bad him come out of the water and make him ready; and Sir Ector anon turned him shortly, and in fewter cast his spear, and smote the other knight a great buffet that his horse turned twice about.

"This was well done," said the strong knight, "and knightly thou hast stricken me."

And therewith he rushed his horse on Sir Ector and caught him under his right arm, and bare him clean out of the saddle, and rode with him away into his own hall, and threw him down in the midst of the floor. The name of this knight was Sir Turquine. Then he said unto Sir Ector:

"For thou hast done this day more unto me than any knight did these twelve years, now will I grant thee thy life, so thou wilt be sworn to be my prisoner all thy life days."

"Nay," said Sir Ector, "that will I never promise thee, but that I will do mine advantage."

"That me repenteth," said Sir Turquine.

And then he made to unarm him, and beat him with thorns all naked, and after put him down in a deep dungeon, where he knew many of his fellows. But when Sir Ector saw Sir Lionel, then made he great sorrow.

"Alas, brother," said Sir Ector, "where is my brother Sir Launcelot?"

"Fair brother, I left him on sleep when that I from him went, under an apple-tree, and what is become of him I cannot tell you."

"Alas," said the knights, "but Sir Launcelot help us we may never be delivered, for we know now no knight that is able to match our master Turquine."

Now leave we these knights prisoners, and speak we of Sir Launcelot du Lake that lieth under the apple-tree sleeping. Even about the noon there came by him four queens of great estate; and, for the heat of the sun should not annoy them, there rode four knights about them and bare a cloth of green silk on four spears, betwixt them and the sun, and the queens rode on four white mules.

Thus as they rode they heard by them a great horse grimly neigh, and then were they ware of a sleeping knight that lay all armed under an apple-tree; anon as these queens looked on his face they knew that it was Sir Launcelot. Then they began for to strive for that knight; everyone said she would have him to her love.

"We shall not strive," said Morgan le Fay, that was King Arthur's sister; "I shall put an enchantment upon him that he shall not awake in six hours, and then I will lead him away unto my castle, and when he is surely within my hold I shall take the enchantment from him, and then let him choose which of us he will have for his love."

So this enchantment was cast upon Sir Launcelot, and then they laid him upon his shield, and bare him so on horseback betwixt two knights, and brought him unto the castle Chariot, and there they laid him in a chamber cold, and at night they sent unto him a fair damsel with his supper ready dight. By that the enchantment was past, and when she came she saluted him, and asked him what cheer? "I cannot say, fair damsel," said Sir Launcelot, "for I wot not how I came into this castle but it be by an enchantment."

"Sir," said she, "ye must make good cheer, and if ye be such a knight as is said ye be, I shall tell you more tomorn by prime of the day."

"Gramercy, fair damsel," said Sir Launcelot, "of your good will I require you."

And so she departed. And there he lay all that night without comfort of anybody.

And on the morn early came these four queens, passingly well beseen, all they bidding him good morn, and he them again.

"Sir knight," the four queens said, "thou must understand thou art our prisoner, and we here know thee well, that thou art Sir Launcelot du Lake, King Ban's son. And truly we understand your worthiness that thou art the noblest knight living; and, as we know well, there can no lady have thy love but one, and that is Queen Guenever, and now thou shalt lose her forever, and she thee, and therefore thee behoveth now to choose one of us four. I am the Queen Morgan le Fay, queen of the land of Gore, and here is the Queen of Northgalis, and the Queen of Eastland, and the Queen of the Out Isles; now choose ye one of us which thou wilt have to thy love, for thou mayst not choose or else in this prison to die."

"This is an hard case," said Sir Launcelot, "that either I must die or else choose one of you, yet had I lever to die in this prison with worship, than to have one of you to my love maugre my head. And therefore ye be answered, for I will have none of you, for ye be false enchantresses. And as for my lady Dame Guenever, were I at my liberty as I was, I would prove it on you or upon yours, that she is the truest lady unto her lord living."

"Well," said the queens, "is this your answer, that you will refuse us?"

"Yea, on my life," said Sir Launcelot, "refused ye be of me."

So they departed and left him there alone that made great sorrow.

Right so at the noon came the damsel unto him with his dinner, and asked him what cheer?

"Truly, fair damsel," said Sir Launcelot, "in my life days never so ill."

"Sir," she said, "that me repenteth, but and ye will be ruled by me I shall help you out of this distress, and ye shall have no shame nor villainy, so that ye hold me a promise."

"Fair damsel, I will grant you, and sore I am of these queens sorceresses afeard, for they have destroyed many a good knight."

"Sir," said she, "that is sooth, and for the renown and bounty they hear of you they would have your love, and, sir, they say your name is Sir Launcelot du Lake, the flower of knights, and they be passing wroth with you that ye have refused them. But, sir, and ye would promise me for to help my father on Tuesday next coming, that hath made a tournament betwixt him and the King of North-galis (for the last Tuesday past my father lost the field through three knights of King Arthur's court), and if ye will be there upon Tuesday next coming and help my father, tomorn ere prime, by the grace of God, I shall deliver you clean."

"Fair maiden," said Sir Launcelot, "tell me what is your father's name, and then shall I give you an answer."

"Sir knight," she said, "my father is King Bagdemagus, that was foul rebuked at the last tournament."

"I know your father well," said Sir Launcelot, "for a noble king and a good knight, and by the faith of my body, ye shall have my body ready to do your father and you service at that day."

"Sir," she said, "gramercy, and tomorn await ye be ready betimes, and I shall be she that shall deliver you, and take you your armor and your horse, shield and spear: and hereby, within this ten mile, is an abbey of white monks, there I pray you that ye me abide, and thither shall I bring my father unto you."

"All this shall be done," said Sir Launcelot, "as I am true knight."

And so she departed, and came on the morn early, and found him ready. Then she brought him out of twelve locks, and brought him unto his armor, and when he was armed clean, she brought him until his own horse, and lightly he saddled him, and took a great spear in his hand, and so rode forth, and said:

"Fair damsel, I shall not fail you by the grace of God."

And so he rode into a great forest all that day, and never could find no highway, and so the night fell on him, and then was he ware in a valley of a pavilion of red sendal.

"By my faith," said Sir Launcelot, "in that pavilion will I lodge all this night."

And so there he alight down, and tied his horse to the pavilion, and there he unarmed him, and there he found a bed, and laid him therein and he fell on sleep heavily.

Then within an hour came the knight to whom belonged the pavilion, and so he laid him down beside Sir Launcelot. And when Sir Launcelot felt him, he started out of the bed lightly, and the other knight after him, and either of them gat their swords in their hands, and out at the pavilion door went the knight of the pavilion, and Sir Launcelot followed him, and there, by a little slake, Sir Launcelot wounded him sore nigh unto the death. And then he yielded him unto Sir Launcelot, and so he granted him, so that he would tell him why he came into the bed.

"Sir," said the knight, "the pavilion is mine own, and there this night would I have slept, and now I am likely to die of this wound."

"That me repenteth," said Sir Launcelot, "of your hurt; but I was adread of treason, for I was late beguiled; and therefore come on your way into your pavilion, and take your rest, and as I suppose I shall stanch your blood."

So they went both into the pavilion, and anon Sir Launcelot stanched his blood.

Therewithal came the knight's lady, which was a passing fair lady. And when she espied that her lord Belleus was so sore wounded, she cried out on Sir Launcelot, and made great dole out of measure.

"Peace, my lady and my love," said Belleus, "for this knight is a good man, and a knight adventurous;" and there he told her all the cause how he was wounded; "and when that I yielded me unto him, he left me goodly and hath stanched my blood."

"Sir," said the lady, "I require thee tell me what knight ye be, and what is your name?"

"Fair lady," said he, "my name is Sir Launcelot du Lake."

"So me thought ever by your speech," said the lady, "for I have seen you oft or this, and I know you better than ye ween. But now and ye would promise me of your courtesy, for the harms that ye have done to me and to my lord Belleus, that when he cometh unto Arthur's court for to cause him to be made knight of the Round Table, for he is a passing good man of arms, and a mighty lord of lands of many out isles."

"Fair lady," said Sir Launcelot, "let him come unto the court the next high feast, and look that ye come with him, and I shall do my power, and ye prove you doughty of your hands, that ye shall have your desire."

So thus within awhile as they thus talked, the night passed, and the day shone, and then Sir Launcelot armed him and took his horse, and they taught him to the abbey, and thither he rode within the space of two hours.

And as soon as Sir Launcelot came within the abbey yard the daughter of King Bagdemagus heard a great horse go on the pavement. And she then arose and went unto a window, and there she saw Sir Launcelot, and anon she made men fast to take his horse from him and let lead him into a stable, and himself was led into a fair chamber, and unarmed him, and the lady sent him a long gown, and anon she came herself. And then she made Launcelot passing good cheer, and she said he was the knight in the world was most welcome to her. Then in all haste she sent for her father Bagdemagus that was within twelve mile of that abbey, and afore even he came with a fair fellowship of knights with him. And when the King was alight off his horse he went straight unto Sir Launcelot's chamber, and there he found his daughter, and then the King embraced Sir Launcelot in his arms, and either made other good cheer. Anon Sir Launcelot made his complaint unto the King how he was betrayed, and how his brother Sir Lionel was departed from him he wist not where, and how his daughter had delivered him out of prison—"therefore while I live I shall do her service and all her kindred."

"Then am I sure of your help," said the King, "on Tuesday next coming."

"Yea, sir," said Sir Launcelot, "I shall not fail you, for so I have promised my lady your daughter. But, sir, what knights been they of my lord Arthur's, that were with the King of Northgalis?"

And the King said: "It was Sir Mador de la Porte, and Sir Mordred, and Sir Gahalatine, that all for-fared my knights, for against them three I nor my knights might bear no strength."

"Sir," said Sir Launcelot, "as I hear say that the tournament shall be within this three mile of this abbey, ye shall send unto me three knights of yours such as ye trust, and look that the three knights have all white shields, and I also, and no painture on the shields, and we four will come out of a little wood in the midst of both parties, and we shall fall in the front of our enemies and grieve them that we may; and thus shall I not be known what knight I am."

So they took their rest that night, and this was on the Sunday. And so the King departed, and sent unto Sir Launcelot three knights, with the four white shields.

And on the Tuesday they lodged them in a little leaved wood beside there the tournament should be. And there were scaffolds and holes that lords and ladies might behold and to give the prize. Then came into the field the King of Northgalis with eightscore helms. And then the three knights of Arthur stood by themselves. Then came into the field King Bagdemagus with forescore of helms. And then they fewtered their spears, and came together with a great dash, and there were slain of knights, at the first recounter, twelve of King Bagdemagus's party, and six of the King of Northgalis's party, and King Bagdemagus's party was far set aback.

With that came Sir Launcelot du Lake, and he thrust in with his spear in the thickest of the press, and there he smote down with one spear five knights, and of four of them he brake their backs. And in that throng he smote down the King of Northgalis, and brake his thigh in that fall. All this doing of Sir Launcelot saw the three knights of Arthur.

"Yonder is a shrewd guest," said Sir Mador de la Porte, "therefore have here once at him."

So they encountered, and Sir Launcelot bare him down horse and man, so that his shoulder went out of joint.

"Now befalleth it to me to just," said Mordred, "for Sir Mador hath a sore fall."

Sir Launcelot was ware of him, and gat a great spear in his hand, and met him, and Sir Mordred brake a spear upon him, and Sir Launcelot gave him such a buffet that the bow of his saddle brake, and so he flew over his horse tail, that his helm went into the earth a foot and more, that nigh his neck was broken, and there he lay long in a swoon. Then came in Sir Gahalatine with a spear, and Launcelot against him, with all their strength that they might drive, that both their spears to-brast even to their hands, and then they flung out with their swords, and gave many a grim stroke. Then was Sir Launcelot wroth out of measure, and then he smote Sir Gahalatine on the helm, that his nose burst out on blood, and ears and

mouth both, and therewith his head hung low. And therewith his
horse ran away with him, and he fell down to the earth.

Anon therewithal Sir Launcelot gat a great spear in his hand,
and, or ever that great spear brake, he bare down to the earth six-
teen knights, some horse and man, and some the man and not the
horse, and there was none but that he hit surely he bare none arms
that day. And then he gat another great spear, and smote down
twelve knights, and the most part of them never throve after. And
then the knights of the King of Northgalis would just no more, and
there the prize was given unto King Bagdemagus. So either party
departed unto his own place, and Sir Launcelot rode forth with
King Bagdemagus unto his castle, and there he had passing good
cheer both with the King and with his daughter, and they proffered
him great gifts. And on the morn he took his leave, and told King
Bagdemagus that he would go and seek his brother Sir Lionel, that
went from him when that he slept. So he took his horse, and betaught them all to God. And there he said unto the King's daughter:
"If ye have need any time of my service, I pray you let me have
knowledge, and I shall not fail you, as I am true knight."

And so Sir Launcelot departed, and by adventure he came into
the same forest where he was taken sleeping. And in the midst
of an highway he met a damsel riding on a white palfrey, and there
either saluted other.

"Fair damsel," said Sir Launcelot, "know ye in this country
any adventures?"

"Sir knight," said that damsel, "here are adventures near hand,
and thou durst prove them."

"Why should I not prove adventures?" said Sir Launcelot; "for
that cause came I hither."

"Well," said she, "thou seemest well to be a good knight, and if
thou dare meet with a good knight, I shall bring thee where is the
best knight and the mightiest that ever thou found, so thou wilt
tell me what is thy name, and what knight thou art."

"Damsel, as for to tell thee my name, I take no great force: truly,
my name is Sir Launcelot du Lake."

"Sir, thou beseemest well, here be adventures by that fall for
thee, for hereby dwelleth a knight that will not be overmatched for
no man that I know, unless ye overmatch him, and his name is Sir
Turquine. And, as I understand, he hath in his prison of Arthur's

court good knights threescore and four that he hath won with his own hands. But when ye have done that day's work ye shall promise me as ye are a true knight for to go with me, and to help me and other damsels that are distressed daily with a false knight."

"All your intent, damsel, and desire I will fulfil, so ye will bring me unto this knight."

"Now, fair knight, come on your way."

And so she brought him unto the ford, and unto the tree where hung the basin. So Sir Launcelot let his horse drink, and then he beat on the basin with the butt of his spear so hard with all his might till the bottom fell out, and long he did so, but he saw nothing. Then he rode endlong the gates of that manor nigh half an hour. And then was he ware of a great knight that drove an horse afore him, and overthwart the horse there lay an armed knight bound. And ever as they came near and near, Sir Launcelot thought he should know him; then Sir Launcelot was ware that it was Sir Gaheris, Gawaine's brother, a knight of the Table Round.

"Now, fair damsel," said Sir Launcelot, "I see yonder cometh a knight fast bound that is a fellow of mine, and brother he is unto Sir Gawaine. And at the first beginning I promise you, by the leave of God, to rescue that knight; and unless his master sit better in the saddle I shall deliver all the prisoners that he hath out of danger, for I am sure that he hath two brethren of mine prisoners with him."

By that time that either had seen other they gripped their spears unto them.

"Now, fair knight," said Sir Launcelot, "put that wounded knight off the horse, and let him rest awhile, and let us two prove our strengths. For as it is informed me, thou doest and hast done great despite and shame unto knights of the Round Table, and therefore now defend thee."

"And thou be of the Table Round," said Turquine, "I defy thee and all thy fellowship."

"That is over-much said," said Sir Launcelot.

And then they put their spears in the rests, and came together with their horses as fast as they might run, and either smote other in the midst of their shields, that both their horses' backs brast under them, and the knights were both astonied, and as soon as they might avoid their horses they took their shields afore them, and drew out their swords, and came together eagerly, and either gave other many strong strokes, for there might neither shields nor harness hold their strokes. And so within awhile they had both grimly wounds, and bled passing grievously. Thus they fared two hours or more, trasing and rasing either other where they might hit any bare place. Then at the last they were breathless both, and stood leaning on their swords.

"Now, fellow," said Sir Turquine, "hold thy hand awhile, and tell me what I shall ask thee."

"Say on."

Then Turquine said: "Thou art the biggest man that ever I met withal, and the best breathed, and like one knight that I hate above all other knights; so be it that thou be not he I will lightly accord with thee, and for thy love I will deliver all the prisoners that I have, that is threescore and four, so thou wilt tell me thy name. And thou and I we will be fellows together, and never to fail the while that I live."

"It is well said," said Sir Launcelot, "but sithen it is so that I may have thy friendship, what knight is he that thou so hatest above all other?"

"Faithfully," said Sir Turquine, "his name is Sir Launcelot du Lake, for he slew my brother Sir Carados at the dolorous tower, that was one of the best knights on live; and therefore him I except of knights, for may I once meet with him the one of us shall make an end of other, I make mine avow. And for Sir Launcelot's sake I have slain an hundred good knights, and as many I have maimed all utterly that they might never after help themselves, and many have died in prison, and yet I have threescore and four, and all shall be delivered, so thou wilt tell me thy name, so it be that thou be not Sir Launcelot."

"Now see I well," said Sir Launcelot, "that such a man I might be that I might have peace; and such a man I might be that there should be war mortal betwixt us: and now, sir knight, at thy request I will that thou wit and know that I am Launcelot du Lake, King Ban's son of Benwick, and very knight of the Table Round. And now I defy thee, do thy best."

"Ah," said Turquine, "Launcelot, thou art unto me most welcome that ever was knight, for we shall never part till the one of us be dead."

Then they hurtled together as two wild bulls, rashing and lashing

with their shields and swords that sometimes they fell both over their
noses. Thus they fought still two hours and more, and never would
have rest, and Sir Turquine gave Sir Launcelot many wounds that
all the ground there as they fought was all bespeckled with blood.

Then at the last Sir Turquine waxed faint, and gave somewhat
aback, and bare his shield low for weariness. That espied Sir Launcelot and leapt upon him fiercely and got him by the beaver of his
helmet, and plucked him down on his knees, and anon he rased
off his helm, and smote his neck in sunder. And when Sir Launcelot
had done this he went unto the damsel and said:

"Damsel, I am ready to go with you where ye will have me, but
I have no horse."

"Fair sir," said she, "take this wounded knight's horse, and send
him into this manor, and command him to deliver all the prisoners."

So Sir Launcelot went unto Gaheris, and prayed him not to be
aggrieved for to lend him his horse.

"Nay, fair lord," said Sir Gaheris, "I will that ye take my horse at
your own commandment, for ye have both saved me and my horse,
and this day I say ye are the best knight in the world, for ye have
slain this day in my sight the mightiest man and the best knight,
except you, that ever I saw; and sir," said Gaheris, "I pray you tell
me your name?"

"Sir, my name is Sir Launcelot du Lake, that ought to help you
of right for King Arthur's sake, and in especial for my lord Sir Gawaine's sake, your own dear brother; and when that ye come within
yonder manor I am sure ye shall find there many knights of the
Round Table, for I have seen many of their shields that I know on
yonder tree. There is Kay's shield, and Sir Brandel's shield, and
Sir Marhaus's shield, and Sir Galind's shield, and Sir Brian Listo-
noise's shield, and Sir Aliduke's shield, with many more that I am
not now advised of, and also my two brethren's shields, Sir Ector de
Maris and Sir Lionel; wherefore I pray you greet them all from me,
and say that I bid them take there such stuff as they find, and that
in any wise my brethren go unto the court and abide me there till
that I come, for by the feast of Pentecost I cast me to be there, for
at this time I must ride with this damsel for to save my promise."

And so he departed from Gaheris, and Sir Gaheris went into the
manor, and there he found a yeoman porter keeping there many
keys. Anon withal Sir Gaheris threw the porter unto the ground

and took the keys from him, and hastily he opened the prison door, and there he let out all the prisoners, and every man loosed other of their bonds. And when they saw Sir Gaheris, all they thanked him, for they wend that he was wounded.

"Not so," said Gaheris, "it was Launcelot that slew him worshipfully with his own hands, I saw it with mine own eyes. And he greeted you all well, and prayeth you to haste you to the court, and as unto Sir Lionel and Ector de Maris, he prayeth you to abide him at the court."

"That shall we not do," said his brethren, "we will find him and we may live."

"So shall I," said Sir Kay, "find him or I come at the court, as I am true knight."

Then all those knights sought the house where as the armor was, and then they armed them, and every knight found his own horse, and all that belonged unto him. And when ever this was done, there came a forester with four horses laden with fat venison.

Anon Sir Kay said: "Here is good meat for us for one meal, for we had not many a day no good repast."

And so that venison was roasted, baked, and sodden, and so after supper some abode there all that night, but Sir Lionel and Ector de Maris and Sir Kay rode after Sir Launcelot to find him if they might.

Now turn we unto Sir Launcelot that rode with the damsel in a fair high way.

"Sir," said the damsel, "here by this way haunteth a knight that distresseth all ladies and gentlewomen, and at the least he robbeth them or ill-useth them."

"What," said Sir Launcelot, "is he a thief and a knight, and a ravisher of women? He doth shame unto the order of knighthood and contrary to his oath, it is a pity that he liveth. But, fair damsel, ye shall ride on afore yourself, and I will keep myself in covert, and if that he trouble you or distress you, I shall be your rescue, and learn him to be ruled as a knight."

So the maid rode on by the way a soft, ambling pace. And within awhile came out that knight on horseback out of the wood, and his page with him, and there he put the damsel from her horse, and then she cried. With that came Launcelot as fast as he might, till he came to that knight, saying: "Oh, thou false knight and traitor unto knighthood, who did learn thee to distress ladies and gentle-women?"

When the knight saw Sir Launcelot thus rebuking him, he answered not, but drew his sword and rode unto Sir Launcelot. And Sir Launcelot threw his spear from him, and drew out his sword, and strake him such a buffet on the helmet that he clave his head and neck unto the throat.

"Now hast thou thy payment that long thou hast deserved."

"That is truth," said the damsel, "for like as Turquine watched to destroy knights, so did this knight attend to destroy and distress ladies, damsels, and gentlewomen, and his name was Sir Peris de Forest Savage."

"Now, damsel," said Sir Launcelot, "will ye any more service of me?"

"Nay, sir," she said, "at this time; but Almighty Jesu preserve you wheresoever ye ride or go, for the courtiest knight thou art and meekest unto all ladies and gentlewomen that now liveth. But one thing, sir knight, me thinketh ye lack, ye that are a knight wifeless, that ye will not love some maiden or gentlewoman, for I could never hear say that ever ye loved any of no manner degree, and that is great pity; but it is noised that ye love Queen Guenever, and that she hath ordained by enchantment that ye shall never love none other but her, nor none other damsel nor lady shall rejoice you; wherefore many in this land, of high estate and low, make great sorrow."

"Fair damsel," said Sir Launcelot, "I may not warn people to speak of me what it pleaseth them: but for to be a wedded man I think it not, for then I must couch with her, and leave arms and tournaments, battles and adventures. And as for to say for to take my pleasance with paramours, that will I refuse in principal for dread of God. For knights that be adulterous, or wanton, shall not be happy nor fortunate unto the wars, for either they shall be overcome with a simpler knight than they be themselves, or else they shall by mishap and their cursedness slay better men than they be themselves; and who that so useth shall be unhappy, and all thing is unhappy that is about them."

And so Sir Launcelot and she departed.

And then he rode in a deep forest two days and more, and had strait lodging. So on the third day he rode over a long bridge, and there start upon him suddenly a passing foul churl, and he smote his horse on the nose that he turned about, and asked him why he rode over that bridge without his licence.

"Why should I not ride this way?" said Sir Launcelot, "I may not ride beside."

"Thou shalt not choose," said the churl, and lashed at him with a great club shod with iron. Then Sir Launcelot drew his sword, and put the stroke aback, and clave his head unto the breast. At the end of the bridge was a fair village, and all the people, men and women, cried on Sir Launcelot and said:

"A worse deed diddest thou never for thyself, for thou hast slain the chief porter of our castle."

Sir Launcelot let them say what they would, and straight he went into the castle; and when he came into the castle he alight, and tied his horse to a ring on the wall; and there he saw a fair green court, and thither he dressed himself, for there him thought was a fair place to fight in. So he looked about, and saw much people in doors and windows, that said:

"Fair knight thou art unhappy."

Anon withal came there upon him two great giants, well armed all save the heads, with two horrible clubs in their hands. Sir Launcelot put his shield afore him, and put the stroke away of the one giant, and with his sword he clave his head asunder. When his fellow saw that, he ran away as he were wood, for fear of the horrible strokes, and Sir Launcelot after him with all his might, and smote him on the shoulder, and clave him to the middle. Then Sir Launcelot went into the hall, and there came afore him threescore ladies and damsels, and all kneeled unto him, and thanked God and him of their deliverance.

"For, sir," said they, "the most part of us have been here this seven year their prisoners, and we have worked all manner of silk works for our meat, and we are all great gentlewomen born, and blessed be the time, knight, that ever thou wert born; for thou hast done the most worship that ever did knight in the world, that will we bear record, and we all pray you to tell us your name, that we may tell our friends who delivered us out of prison."

"Fair damsels," he said, "my name is Sir Launcelot du Lake."

"Ah, sir," said they all, "well mayest thou be he, for else save yourself, as we deemed, there might never knight have the better of these two giants, for many fair knights have essayed it, and here have ended, and many times have we wished after you, and these two giants dread never knight but you."

"Now may ye say," said Sir Launcelot, "unto your friends, how and who hath delivered you, and greet them all from me, and if that I come in any of your marches, shew me such cheer as ye have cause; and what treasure that there is in this castle I give it you for a reward for your grievance: and the lord that is the owner of this castle I would that he received it as is right."

"Fair sir," said they, "the name of this castle is Tintagil, and a duke owned it some time that had wedded fair Igraine, and after wedded her Uther Pendragon and gat on her Arthur."

"Well," said Sir Launcelot, "I understand to whom this castle belongeth."

And so he departed from them and betaught them unto God. And then he mounted upon his horse, and rode into many strange and wild countries and through many waters and valleys, and evil was he lodged. And at the last by fortune him happened against a night to come to a fair courtelage, and therein he found an old gentlewoman that lodged him with a good will, and there he had good cheer for him and his horse. And when time was, his host brought him into a fair garret over the gate to his bed. There Sir Launcelot unarmed him, and set his harness by him, and went to bed and anon he fell on sleep. So soon after there came one on horseback, and knocked at the gate in great haste. And when Sir Launcelot heard this he arose up, and looked out at the window, and saw by the moonlight three knights came riding after that one man, and all three lashed on him at once with swords, and that one knight turned on them knightly again and defended him.

"Truly," said Sir Launcelot, "yonder one knight shall I help, for it were shame for me to see three knights on one, and if he be slain I am partner of his death."

And therewith he took his harness and went out at a window by a sheet down to the four knights, and then Sir Launcelot said on high:

"Turn you knights unto me and leave your fighting with that knight."

And then they all three left Sir Kay, and turned unto Sir Launcelot, and there began great battle, for they alight all three, and strake many great strokes at Sir Launcelot, and assailed him on every side.

Then Sir Kay dressed him for to have holpen Sir Launcelot.

"Nay, sir," said he, "I will none of your help, therefore as ye will have my help let me alone with them."

Sir Kay for the pleasure of the knight suffered him for to do his will, and so stood aside. And then anon within six strokes Sir Launcelot had stricken them to the earth.

And then they all three cried: "Sir knight, we yield us unto you as man of might matchless."

"As to that," said Sir Launcelot, "I will not take your yielding unto me, but so that ye yield you unto Sir Kay the seneschal: on that covenant I will save your lives and else not."

"Fair knight," said they, "that were we loth to do; for as for Sir Kay we chased him hither, and had overcome him had not ye been; therefore to yield us unto him it were no reason."

"Well, as to that," said Sir Launcelot, "advise you well, for ye may choose whether ye will die or live, for and ye be yielden it shall be unto Sir Kay."

"Fair knight," then they said, "in saving our lives we will do as thou commandest us."

" Then shall ye," said Sir Launcelot, "on Whitsunday next coming go unto the court of King Arthur, and there shall ye yield you unto Queen Guenever, and put you all three in her grace and mercy, and say that Sir Kay sent you thither to be her prisoners."

"Sir," they said, "it shall be done by the faith of our bodies, and we be living."

And there they swore, every knight upon his sword. And so Sir Launcelot suffered them so to depart. And then Sir Launcelot knocked at the gate with the pommel of his sword, and with that came his host, and in they entered, Sir Kay and he.

"Sir," said his host, "I wend ye had been in your bed."

"So I was," said Sir Launcelot, "but I arose and leapt out at my window for to help an old fellow of mine."

And so when they came nigh the light Sir Kay knew well that it was Sir Launcelot, and therewith he kneeled down and thanked him of all his kindness that he hath holpen him twice from the death.

"Sir," he said, "I have done nothing but that I ought to do, and ye are welcome, and here shall ye repose you and take your rest."

So when Sir Kay was unarmed he asked after meat, so there was meat fetched him, and he ate strongly. And when he had

and departed, and thanked God that he had escaped that adventure.

So Sir Launcelot rode throughout marshes and many wild ways. And as he rode in a valley he saw a knight chasing a lady with a naked sword to have slain her. And by fortune, as this knight should have slain this lady, she cried on Sir Launcelot and prayed him to rescue her. When Sir Launcelot saw that mischief he took his horse and rode between them, saying:

"Knight, fie for shame; why wilt thou slay this lady? Thou dost shame unto thee and all knights."

"What hast thou to do betwixt me and my wife?" said the knight; "I will slay her, maugre thy head."

"That shall ye not," said Sir Launcelot, "for rather we two will have ado together."

"Sir Launcelot," said the knight, "thou doest not thy part, for this lady hath betrayed me."

"It is not so," said the lady; "truly he saith wrong on me, and because I love and cherish my cousin german, he is jealous betwixt him and me, and as I shall answer to God, there was never sin betwixt us. But, sir," said the lady, "as thou art called the worshipfulest knight of the world, I require thee of true knighthood keep me and save me, for whatsoever ye say he will slay me, for he is without mercy."

"Have ye no doubt," said Launcelot, "it shall not lie in his power."

"Sir," said the knight, "in your sight I will be ruled as ye will have me."

And so Sir Launcelot rode on the one side and she on the other; he had not ridden but a while but the knight bade Sir Launcelot turn him and look behind him and said:

"Sir, yonder come men of arms after us riding."

And so Sir Launcelot turned him, and thought no treason. And therewith was the knight and the lady on one side, and suddenly he swapped off his lady's head. And when Sir Launcelot had espied him what he had done, he said, and called him:

"Traitor, thou hast shamed me forever."

And suddenly Sir Launcelot alight off his horse, and pulled out his sword to slay him. And therewithal he fell flat to the earth, and gripped Sir Launcelot by the thighs, and cried mercy.

"Fie on thee," said Sir Launcelot, "thou shameful knight, thou mayest have no mercy, and therefore arise and fight with me."

"Nay," said the knight, "I will never arise till ye grant me mercy."

"Now will I proffer thee fair," said Launcelot; "I will unarm me unto my shirt, and will have nothing upon me but my shirt, and my sword in my hand, and if thou canst slay me quit be thou forever."

"Nay, sir," said Pedivere, "that will I never."

"Well," said Sir Launcelot, "take this lady and the head, and bear it upon thee, and here shalt thou swear upon my sword to bear it alway upon thy back, and never to rest till thou come to Queen Guenever."

"Sir," said he, "that will I do, by the faith of my body."

"Now," said Launcelot, "tell me what is your name."

"Sir, my name is Pedivere."

"In a shameful hour wert thou born," said Launcelot.

So Pedivere departed with the dead lady and the head, and found the Queen with King Arthur at Winchester, and there he told all the truth.

"Sir knight," said the Queen, "this is an horrible deed and a shameful, and a great rebuke unto Sir Launcelot: but notwithstanding his worship is not known in divers countries. But this shall I give you in penance: make ye as good skift as ye can, ye shall bear this lady with you on horseback unto the Pope of Rome, and of him receive your penance for your foul deeds, and ye shall never rest one night there as ye do another, and if ye go to any bed the dead body shall lie with you."

This oath there he made, and so departed, and as it telleth in the French book, when he came to Rome the Pope bade him go again to Queen Guenever, and in Rome was his lady buried by the Pope's commandment. And after this Sir Pedivere fell to great goodness, and was an holy man and an hermit.

Now turn me unto Sir Launcelot du Lake, that came home two days afore the feast of Pentecost. And the King and all the court were passing fain of his coming. And when Sir Gawaine, Sir Uwaine, Sir Sagramour, Sir Ector de Maris, saw Sir Launcelot in Kay's armor, then they wist well it was he that smote them down all with one spear. Then there was laughing and smiling among them. And ever now and now came all the knights home that Sir Turquine had prisoners, and they all honored and worshiped Sir Launcelot. When Sir Gaheris heard them speak, he said:

"I saw all the battle from the beginning to the ending," and there he told King Arthur all how it was, and how Sir Turquine was the strongest knight that ever he saw except Sir Launcelot: there were many knights bear him record, nigh threescore.

Then Sir Kay told the King how Sir Launcelot had rescued him when he should have been slain, and how he made the knights yield them to me, and not to him. And there they were, all three, and bare record.

"And by my faith," said Sir Kay, "because Sir Launcelot took my harness and left me his I rode in good peace, and no man would have ado with me."

Anon therewithal came the three knights that fought with Sir Launcelot at the long bridge, and there they yielded them unto Sir Kay, and Sir Kay forsook them and said he fought never with them:

"But I shall ease your hearts," said Sir Kay; "yonder is Sir Launcelot that overcame you."

When they wist that they were glad.

And then Sir Meliot de Logres came home, and told King Arthur how Sir Launcelot had saved him from the death. And all his deeds were known, how four queens, sorceresses, had him in prison, and how he was delivered by King Bagdemagus's daughter. Also there were told all the great deeds of arms that Sir Launcelot did betwixt the two kings, that is to say, the King of Northgalis and King Bagdemagus. All the truth Sir Gahalantine did tell, and Sir Mador de la Porte, and Sir Mordred, for they were at that same tournament.

Then came in the lady that knew Sir Launcelot when that he wounded Sir Belleus at the pavilion. And there, at the request of Sir Launcelot, Sir Belleus was made knight of the Round Table.

And so at that time Sir Launcelot had the greatest name of any knight of the world, and most he was honored of high and low.

Launcelot and Guenever. In May, when every lusty heart flourisheth and burgeneth; for as the season is lusty to behold and comfortable, so man and woman rejoice and gladden of summer coming with his fresh flowers: for winter with his rough winds and blasts, causeth a lusty man and woman to cower and sit fast by the fire. So in this season, as in the month of May, it befell a great anger and unhap that stinted not till the flower of chivalry of all the world was destroyed and slain: and all was long upon two unhappy knights, the which were named Sir Agravaine and Sir Mordred that were brethren unto Sir Gawaine. For this Sir Agravaine and Sir Mordred had ever a privy hate unto the Queen, Dame Guenever, and to Sir Launcelot, and daily and nightly they ever watched upon Sir Launcelot. So it mishapped Sir Gawaine and all his brethren were in King Arthur's chamber, and then Sir Agravaine said thus openly, and not in no counsel, that many knights might hear it:

"I marvel that we all be not ashamed both to see and to know how Sir Launcelot goeth with the Queen, and all we know it so, and it is shamefully suffered of us all, that we all should suffer so noble a king as King Arthur is so to be shamed."

Then spake Sir Gawaine, and said: "Brother, Sir Agravaine, I pray you, and charge you, move no such matters no more afore me; for wit ye well, I will not be of your counsel."

"Truly," said Sir Gaheris and Sir Gareth, "we will not be knowing, brother Agravaine, of your deeds."

"Then will I," said Sir Mordred.

"I believe well that," said Sir Gawaine, "forever, unto all unhappiness, brother Sir Mordred, thereto will ye grant, and I would that ye left all this, and made you not so busy, for I know what will fall of it."

"Fall of it what fall may," said Sir Agravaine, "I will disclose it to the King."

"Not by my counsel," said Sir Gawaine, "for and there rise war and wrake betwixt Sir Launcelot and us, wit you well, brother, there will many kings and great lords hold with Sir Launcelot. Also, brother Sir Agravaine," said Sir Gawaine, "ye must remember how ofttimes Sir Launcelot hath rescued the King and the Queen, and the best of us all had been full cold at the heart-root, had not Sir Launcelot been better than we; and that hath he proved himself full oft. And as for my part, I will never be against Sir Launcelot, for one day's deed, when he rescued me from King Carados of the dolorous tower, and slew him, and saved my life. Also, brother Sir Agravaine, and Sir Mordred, in likewise Sir Launcelot rescued you both, and threescore and two, from Sir Turquine. Me thinketh, brother, such kind deeds and kindness should be remembered."

"Do as ye list," said Sir Agravaine, "for I will hide it no longer."
With these words came to them King Arthur.

"Now, brother, stint your noise," said Sir Gawaine.

"We will not," said Sir Agravaine and Sir Mordred.

"Will ye so?" said Sir Gawaine, "then God speed you, for I will not hear your tales, nor be of your counsel."

"No more will I," said Sir Gareth and Sir Gaheris, "for we will never say evil by that man: for because," said Sir Gareth, "Sir Launcelot made me knight, by no manner ought I to say ill of him."

And therewithal they three departed, making great dole.

"Alas," said Sir Gawaine and Sir Gareth, "now is this realm wholly mischieved, and the noble fellowship of the Round Table shall be dispersed."

So they departed.

And then King Arthur asked them what noise they made.

"My lord," said Agravaine, "I shall tell you that I may keep no longer. Here is I and my brother, Sir Mordred, brake unto my brother Sir Gawaine, Sir Gaheris, and to Sir Gareth, how this we know all, that Sir Launcelot holdeth your Queen, and hath done long, and we be your sister's sons, and we may suffer it no longer; and all we wot that ye should be above Sir Launcelot, and ye are the King that made him knight, and, therefore, we will prove it that he is a traitor to your person."

"If it be so," said King Arthur, "wit you well he is none other, but I would be loth to begin such a thing, but I might have proofs upon it; for Sir Launcelot is an hardy knight, and all ye know he is the best knight among us all, and, but if he be taken with the deed, he will fight with him that bringeth up the noise, and I know no knight that is able to match him. Therefore, and it be sooth as ye say, I would he were taken with the deed."

For the King was full loth thereto, that any noise should be upon Sir Launcelot and his Queen; for the King had a deeming, but he would not hear of it, for Sir Launcelot had done so much for him and for the Queen so many times, that, wit ye well, the King loved him passingly well.

"My lord," said Sir Agravaine, "ye shall ride to-morrow on hunting, and doubt ye not, Sir Launcelot will not go with you. Then when it draweth toward night, ye may send the Queen word that ye will lie out all that night, and so may ye send for your cooks; and then, upon pain of death, we shall take him with the Queen, and either we shall bring him to you dead or quick."

"I will well," said the King, "then I counsel you, take with you sure fellowship."

"Sir," said Agravaine, "my brother, Sir Mordred, and I will take with us twelve knights of the Round Table."

"Beware," said King Arthur, "for I warn you ye shall find him wight."

"Let us deal," said Sir Agravaine and Sir Mordred.

So on the morn, King Arthur rode on hunting, and sent word to the Queen that he would be out all that night.

Then Sir Agravaine and Sir Mordred gat to them twelve knights, and did themselves in a chamber, in the castle of Carlisle, and these were their names: Sir Colgrevance, Sir Mador de la Porte, Sir Gingaline, Sir Meliot de Logris, Sir Petipase of Winchelsea, Sir Galleron of Galway, Sir Melion of the Mountain, Sir Astamore, Sir Gromore Somir Joure, Sir Curselaine, Sir Florence, Sir Lovel.

So these twelve knights were with Sir Mordred and Sir Agravaine. And all they were of Scotland, either of Sir Gawaine's kin, either well willers to his brethren. So when the night came, Sir Launcelot told Sir Bors how he would go that night and speak with the Queen.

"Sir," said Sir Bors, "ye shall not go this night, by my counsel."

"Why?" said Sir Launcelot.

"Sir," said Sir Bors, "I dread me ever of Sir Agravaine, that waiteth you daily, to do you shame, and us all, and never gave my heart against no going that ever ye went to the Queen, so much as now, for I mistrust that the King is out this night from the Queen, because, peradventure, he hath lain some watch for you and the Queen, and therefore I dread me sore of treason."

"Have ye no dread," said Sir Launcelot, "for I shall go, and come again, and make no tarrying."

"Sir," said Sir Bors, "that me sore repenteth, for I dread me sore that your going out this night shall wrath us all."

"Fair nephew," said Sir Launcelot, "I marvel me much why ye say thus, sithen the Queen hath sent for me, and wit ye well that I will not be so much a coward, but she shall understand I will see her good grace."

"God speed you well," said Sir Bors. "and send you sound and safe again."

So Sir Launcelot departed, and took his sword under his arm, and so in his mantle that noble knight put himself in great jeopardy, and so he passed till he came to the Queen's chamber. And then there came Sir Agravaine, and Sir Mordred, with twelve knights with them of the Round Table, and they said with crying voice: "Traitor knight, Sir Launcelot du Lake, now art thou taken."

And thus they cried with a loud voice that all the court might hear it: and they all fourteen were armed at all points as they should fight in a battle.

"Alas," said Queen Guenever, "now are we mischieved both."

"Madam," said Sir Launcelot, "is there here any armor within your chamber that I might cover my poor body withal; and if there be any give it me, and I shall soon stint their malice."

"Truly," said the Queen, "I have none armor, shield, sword, nor spear, wherefore I dread me sore our long love is come to a mischievous end; for, I hear by their noise, there be many noble knights, and well I wot they be surely armed, against them ye may make no resistance; wherefore ye are likely to be slain, and then shall I be burnt. For, and ye might escape them, I would not doubt but that ye would rescue me in what danger that ever I stood in."

"Alas," said Sir Launcelot, "in all my life was I never bested that I should be thus shamefully slain for lack of mine armor."

But ever in one Sir Agravaine and Sir Mordred cried:

"Traitor knight, come out of the Queen's chamber, for wit thou well thou art so beset that thou shalt not escape."

"O mercy," said Sir Launcelot, "this shameful cry and noise I may not suffer, for better were death at once than thus to endure this pain."

Then he took the Queen in his arms and kissed her, and said:

"Most noble Christian Queen, I beseech you, as ye have ever been my special good lady, and I at all times your true poor knight unto my power, and as I never failed you in right nor in wrong, since the first day that King Arthur made me knight, that ye will pray for my soul if that I here be slain. For well I am well assured that Sir Bors, my nephew, and all the remnant of my kin, with Sir Lavaine and Sir Urre, that they will not fail you to rescue you from the fire, and therefore, mine own lady, recomfort yourself whatsoever come of me, that ye go with Sir Bors, my nephew, and Sir Urre, and they all will do you all the pleasure that they can or may, that ye shall live like a queen upon my lands."

"Nay, Launcelot," said the Queen, "wit thou well I will never live after thy days, but, and thou be slain, I will take my death as meekly for Jesu Christ's sake, as ever did any Christian queen."

"Well, madam," said Launcelot, "sith it is so that the day is come that our love must depart, wit you well I shall sell my life as dear as I may, and a thousandfold. I am more heavier for you than for myself. And now I had lever than to be lord of all Christendom, that I had sure armor upon me, that men might speak of my deeds or ever I were slain."

"Truly," said the Queen, "I would and it might please God that they would take me and slay me, and suffer you to escape."

"That shall never be," said Sir Launcelot. "God defend me from such a shame, but Jesu be thou my shield and mine armor."

And therewith Sir Launcelot wrapped his mantle about his arm well and surely; and by then they had gotten a great form out of the hall, and therewithal they rashed at the door.

"Fair lords," said Sir Launcelot, "leave your noise and your rashing, and I shall set open this door, and then may ye do with me what it liketh you."

"Come off then," said they all, "and do it, for it availeth thee not to strive against us all, and therefore let us into this chamber, and we shall save thy life until thou come to King Arthur."

Then Launcelot unbarred the door, and with his left hand he held it open a little so that but one man might come in at once. And so anon, there came striding a good knight, a much man and large, and his name was Colgrevance of Gore, and he with a sword strake at Sir Launcelot mightily, and he put aside the stroke, and gave him such a buffet upon the helmet that he fell groveling dead within the chamber door, and then Sir Launcelot with great might drew that dead knight within the chamber door; and then Sir Launcelot, with the help of the Queen and her ladies, was lightly armed in Sir Colgrevance's armor. And ever stood Sir Agravaine and Sir Mordred, crying:

"Traitor knight, come out of the Queen's chamber."

"Leave your noise," said Sir Launcelot unto Sir Agravaine, "for wit ye well, Sir Agravaine, ye shall not prison me this night, and therefore and ye do by my counsel, go ye all from this chamber door,

I came in this realm that should be thus shamefully banished, undeserved and causeless. But fortune is so variant, and the wheel so movable, there is no constant abiding, and that may be proved by many old chronicles of noble Hector, and Troilus, and Alisander the mighty conqueror, and many other more. When they were most in their royalty, they alight lowest; and so fareth by me," said Sir Launcelot, "for in this realm I had worship, and by me and mine all the whole Round Table hath been increased more in worship by me and my blood than by any other."

The Death of Arthur. As Sir Mordred was ruler of all England, he did do make letters as though that they came from beyond the sea, and the letters specified that King Arthur was slain in battle with Sir Launcelot. Wherefore Sir Mordred made a Parliament, and called the lords together, and there he made them to choose him King, and so was he crowned at Canterbury, and held a feast there fifteen days, and afterward he drew him unto Winchester, and there he took the Queen Guenever, and said plainly that he would wed her which was his uncle's wife, and his father's wife. And so he made ready for the feast, and a day prefixed that they should be wedded; wherefore Queen Guenever was passing heavy. But she durst not discover her heart, but spake fair, and agreed to Sir Mordred's will. Then she desired of Sir Mordred for to go to London, to buy all manner of things that longed unto the wedding. And because of her fair speech Sir Mordred trusted her well enough, and gave her leave to go. And so when she came to London, she took the Tower of London, and suddenly, in all haste possible, she stuffed it with all manner of victual, and well garnished it with men, and so kept it. Then when Sir Mordred wist and understood how he was beguiled, he was passing wroth out of measure. And a short tale for to make, he went and laid a mighty siege about the Tower of London, and made many great assaults thereat, and threw many great engines unto them, and shot great guns. But all might not prevail Sir Mordred, for Queen Guenever would never, for fair speech nor for foul, would never trust to come in his hands again. And then came the Bishop of Canterbury, the which was a noble clerk and an holy man, and thus he said to Sir Mordred:

"Sir, what will ye do, will ye first displease God, and sithen shame yourself and all knighthood? Is not King Arthur your uncle, no further but your mother's brother, and are ye not his son, therefore how may ye wed your father's wife? Sir," said the noble clerk, "leave this opinion, or else I shall curse you with book, and bell, and candle."

"Do thou thy worst," said Sir Mordred, "wit thou well I shall defy thee."

"Sir," said the bishop, "and wit you well I shall not fear me to do that me ought to do. Also where ye noise where my lord Arthur is slain, and that is not so, and therefore ye will make a foul work in this land."

As Sir Mordred was at Dover with his host, there came King Arthur with a great navy of ships, galleys, and carracks. And there was Sir Mordred ready awaiting upon his landage, to let his own father to land upon the land that he was king over. Then there was launching of great boats and small, and full of noble men of arms, and there was much slaughter of gentle knights, and many a full bold baron was laid full low on both parties. But King Arthur was so courageous, that there might no manner of knights let him to land, and his knights fiercely followed him. And so he landed, maugre Sir Mordred and all his power, and put Sir Mordred aback, that he fled and all his people. So when this battle was done, King Arthur let bury his people that were dead, and then was the noble knight, Sir Gawaine, found in a great boat lying more than half dead.

Then the King commanded Sir Lucan de butlere, and his brother, Sir Bedivere, with two bishops with them, and charged them in any wise and they might take a treaty for a month day with Sir Mordred.

"And spare not, proffer him lands and goods, as much as ye think best."

So then they departed, and came to Sir Mordred, where he had a grim host of an hundred thousand men. And there they intreated Sir Mordred long time, and at the last Sir Mordred was agreed for to have Cornwall and Kent, by King Arthur's days; after, all England, after the days of King Arthur.

Then were they condescended that King Arthur and Sir Mordred should meet betwixt both their hosts, and every each of them should bring fourteen persons. And they came with this word unto King Arthur. Then said he, "I am glad that this is done." And so he went into the field. And when Arthur should depart, he warned all his host that and they see any sword drawn, "Look ye come on fiercely, and slay that traitor, Sir Mordred, for I in no wise trust him."

In like wise Sir Mordred warned his host that:

"And ye see any sword drawn, look that ye come on fiercely, and so slay all that ever before you standeth: for in no wise I will not trust for this treaty: for I know well my father will be avenged upon me."

And so they met as their pointment was, and so they were agreed and accorded thoroughly: and wine was fetched, and they drank. Right so came an adder out of a little heath bush, and it stung a knight on the foot. And when the knight felt him stungen, he looked down and saw the adder, and then he drew his sword to slay the adder, and thought of none other harm. And when the host on both parties saw that sword drawn, then they blew beames, trumpets, and horns, and shouted grimly. And so both hosts dressed them together. And King Arthur took his horse, and said, "Alas, this unhappy day," and so rode to his party: and Sir Mordred in like wise.

And never was there seen a more dolefuller battle in no Christian land. For there was but rushing and riding, foining and striking, and many a grim word was there spoken either to other, and many a deadly stroke. But ever King Arthur rode throughout the battle of Sir Mordred many times, and did full nobly as a noble king should; and at all times he fainted never. And Sir Mordred that day put him in devoir, and in great peril. And thus they fought all the long day, and never stinted, till the noble knights were laid to the cold ground, and ever they fought still, till it was near night, and by that time was there an hundred thousand laid dead upon the down.

Then was Arthur wroth out of measure, when he saw his people so slain from him. Then the King looked about him, and then was he ware of all his host, and of all his good knights, were left no more on live but two knights, that was Sir Lucan de butlere, and his brother, Sir Bedivere: and they full were sore wounded.

"Jesu, mercy," said the King, "where are all my noble knights becomen? Alas, that ever I should see this doleful day! For now," said Arthur, "I am come to mine end. But would to God that I wist where were that traitor, Sir Mordred, that hath caused all this mischief."

Then was King Arthur ware where Sir Mordred leaned upon his sword among a great heap of dead men.

"Now give me my spear," said Arthur unto Sir Lucan, "for yonder I have espied the traitor that all this wo hath wrought."

"Sir, let him be," said Sir Lucan, "for he is unhappy: and if ye pass this unhappy day, ye shall be right well revenged upon him. Good lord, remember ye of your night's dream, and what the spirit of Sir Gawaine told you this night, yet God of His great goodness hath preserved you hitherto. Therefore, for God's sake, my lord, leave off by this. For blessed be God ye have won the field: for here we be three on live, and with Sir Mordred is none on live. And if ye leave off now, this wicked day of destiny is past."

"Tide me death, betide me life," saith the King, "now I see him yonder alone; he shall never escape mine hands, for at a better avail shall I never have him."

"God speed you well," said Sir Bedivere.

Then the King gat his spear in both his hands, and ran toward Sir Mordred, crying:

"Traitor, now is thy death day come."

And when Sir Mordred heard Sir Arthur, he ran until him with his sword drawn in his hand. And then King Arthur smote Sir Mordred under the shield, with a foin of his spear throughout the body more than a fathom. And when Sir Mordred felt that he had his death's wound, he thrust himself, with the might that he had, up to the bur of King Arthur's spear. And right so he smote his father Arthur with his sword holden in both his hands, on the side of the head, that the sword pierced the helmet and the brain-pan, and therewithal Sir Mordred fell stark dead to the earth. And the noble Arthur fell in a swoon to the earth, and there he swooned ofttimes. And Sir Lucan de butlere and Sir Bedivere ofttimes heaved him up, and so weakly they led him betwixt them both to a little chapel not far from the seaside. And when the King was there, he thought him well eased. Then heard they people cry in the field.

"Now go thou, Sir Lucan," said the King, "and do me to wit what betokens that noise in the field."

So Sir Lucan departed, for he was grievously wounded in many places. And so as he went, he saw and hearkened by the moonlight, how the pillers and robbers were come into the field to pill and to rob many a full noble knight of broaches and beads, of many a good ring, and of many a rich jewel; and who that were not dead all out, there they slew them for their harness and their riches. When Sir Lucan understood this work, he came to the King as soon as he might, and told him all what he had heard and seen.

"Therefore, by mine advice," said Sir Lucan, "it is best that we bring you to some town."

"I would it were so," said the King, "but I may not stand, my head works so. Ah, Sir Launcelot, this day have I sore missed thee. Alas, that ever I was against thee, for now have I my death, whereof Sir Gawaine me warned in my dream."

Then Sir Lucan took up the King the one part, and Sir Bedivere the other part, and in the lifting, the King swooned, and Sir Lucan fell in a swoon with the lift, that the part of his bowels fell out of his body, and therewith the noble knight's heart brast.

And when King Arthur came to himself again, he beheld Sir Lucan how he lay foaming at the mouth, and part of his bowels lay at his feet.

"Alas," said the King, "this is unto me a full heavy sight to see this noble duke so die for my sake, for he would have holpen me that had more need of help than I. Alas, he would not complain him, his heart was so set to help me. Now Jesu have mercy upon his soul."

Then Sir Bedivere wept for the death of his brother.

"Leave this mourning and weeping," said the King, "for all this will not avail me: for, wit thou well, and I might live myself the death of Sir Lucan would grieve me evermore; but my time hieth fast," said the King. "Therefore, take thou Excalibur, my good sword, and go with it to yonder waterside, and when thou comest there, I charge thee throw my sword in that water, and come again, and tell me what thou there seest."

"My lord," said Bedivere, "your commandment shall be done, and lightly bring you word again."

So Sir Bedivere departed, and by the way he beheld that noble sword, that the pommel and haft were all of precious stones, and then he said to himself:

"If I throw this rich sword in the water, thereof shall never come good, but harm and loss."

And then Sir Bedivere hid Excalibur under a tree. And as soon as he might he came again unto the King, and said he had been at the water, and had thrown the sword into the water.

"What sawest thou there?" said the King.

"Sir," he said, "I saw nothing but waves and winds."

"That is untruly said of thee," said the King; "therefore go thou lightly again, and do my command as thou art to me lief and dear, spare not, but throw it in."

Then Sir Bedivere returned again, and took the sword in his hand; and then him thought sin and shame to throw away that noble sword; and so eft he hid the sword, and returned again, and told to the King that he had been at the water, and done his commandment.

"What saw thou there?" said the King.

"Sir," he said, "I saw nothing but the waters wap and the waves wan."

"Ah, traitor, untrue," said King Arthur, "now hast thou betrayed me twice. Who would have wend that thou that hast been to me so lief and dear, and thou art named a noble knight, and would betray me for the riches of the sword. But now go again lightly, for thy long tarrying putteth me in great jeopardy of my life, for I have taken cold. And but if thou do now as I bid thee, if ever I may see thee, I shall slay thee with mine own hands, for thou wouldest for my rich sword see me dead."

Then Sir Bedivere departed, and went to the sword, and lightly took it up, and went to the waterside, and there he bound the girdle about the hilts, and then he threw the sword as far into the water as he might, and there came an arm and an hand above the water, and met it, and caught it, and so shook it thrice and brandished, and then vanished away the hand with the sword in the water.

So Sir Bedivere came again to the King, and told him what he saw.

"Alas," said the King, "help me hence, for I dread me I have tarried over-long."

Then Sir Bedivere took the King upon his back, and so went with him to that waterside. And when they were at the waterside, even fast by the bank hoved a little barge, with many fair ladies in it, and among them all was a queen, and all they had black hoods, and all they wept and shrieked when they saw King Arthur.

"Now put me into the barge," said the King: and so he did softly. And there received him three queens with great mourning, and so they set him down, and in one of their laps King Arthur laid his head, and then that queen said:

"Ah, dear brother, why have ye tarried so long from me? Alas, this wound on your head hath caught over-much cold."

· And so then they rowed from the land; and Sir Bedivere beheld all those ladies go from him. Then Sir Bedivere cried:

"Ah, my lord Arthur, what shall become of me now ye go from me, and leave me here alone among mine enemies?"

"Comfort thyself," said the King, "and do as well as thou mayest, for in me is no trust for to trust in. For I will into the vale of Avilion, to heal me of my grievous wound. And if thou hear never more of me, pray for my soul."

But ever the queens and the ladies wept and shrieked, that it was pity to hear. And as soon as Sir Bedivere had lost the sight of the barge, he wept and wailed, and so took the forest.

The Last Days of Launcelot and Guenever. Then came Sir Bors de Ganis, and said:

"My lord Sir Launcelot, what think ye for to do, now to ride in this realm? wit thou well ye shall find few friends."

"Be as be may," said Sir Launcelot, "keep you still here, for I will forth on my journey, and no man nor child shall go with me."

So it was no boot to strive, but he departed and rode westerly, and there he sought a seven or eight days, and at the last he came to a nunnery, and then was Queen Guenever ware of Sir Launcelot as he walked in the cloister, and when she saw him there she swooned thrice, that all the ladies and gentlewomen had work enough to hold the Queen up. So when she might speak, she called ladies and gentlewomen to her, and said:

"Ye marvel, fair ladies, why I make this fare. Truly, it is for the sight of yonder knight that yonder standeth: wherefore, I pray you all, call him to me."

When Sir Launcelot was brought to her, then she said to all the ladies:

"Through this man and me hath all this war been wrought, and the death of the most noblest knights of the world; for through our love that we have loved together is my most noble lord slain. Therefore, Sir Launcelot, wit thou well I am set in such a plight to get my soul's health; and yet I trust, through God's grace, that after my death to have a sight of the blessed face of Christ, and at doomsday to sit on his right side, for as sinful as ever I was are saints in heaven. Therefore, Sir Launcelot, I require thee and beseech thee heartily, for all the love that ever was betwixt us, that thou never see me more in the visage; and I command thee on God's behalf, that thou forsake my company, and to thy kingdom thou turn again and keep well thy realm from war and wrack. For as well as I have loved thee, mine heart will not serve me to see thee; for through thee and me is the flower of kings and knights destroyed. Therefore, Sir Launcelot, go to thy realm, and there take thee a wife, and live with her with joy and bliss, and I pray thee heartily pray for me to our Lord, that I may amend my mis-living."

"Now, sweet madam," said Sir Launcelot, "would ye that I should return again unto my country, and there to wed a lady? Nay, madam, wit you well that shall I never do: for I shall never be so false to you of that I have promised, but the same destiny that ye have taken you to, I will take me unto, for to please Jesu, and ever for you I cast me specially to pray."

"If thou wilt do so," said the Queen, "hold thy promise; but I may never believe but that thou wilt turn to the world again."

"Well, madam," said he, "ye say as pleaseth you, yet wist you me never false of my promise, and God defend but I should forsake the world as ye have done. For in the quest of the Sancgreal I had forsaken the vanities of the world, had not your lord been. And if I had done so at that time with my heart, will, and thought, I had passed all the knights that were in the Sancgreal, except Sir Galahad my son. And therefore, lady, sithen ye have taken you to perfection, I must needs take me to perfection of right. For I take record of God, in you I have had mine earthly joy. And if I had found you now so disposed, I had cast me to have had you into mine own realm. But sithen I find you thus disposed, I insure you faithfully I will ever take me to penance, and pray while my life lasteth, if that I may find any hermit either gray or white that will receive me. Wherefore, madam, I pray you kiss me, and never no more."

"Nay," said the Queen, "that shall I never do, but abstain you from such works."

And they departed. But there was never so hard an hearted man, but he would have wept to see the dolor that they made. For there was lamentation as they had been stung with spears, and many times they swooned. And the ladies bear the Queen to her chamber,

offered Aiva to the sea-god. Now the children of the first wife grew up to be such favorites with the people of the goddess Danu that Aiva became jealous, especially as she was childless herself. She tried, but unsuccessfully, to persuade her attendants to murder them. Then she took them to Lake Darvra (now Loch Derravargh in West Meath), and sent them into the water to bathe.

The people of the goddess Danu frequently visited the swans on Lake Darvra. The Milesians, after their victory over the elder gods, also visited them, for it was not until long afterward that gods and men ceased to associate, and, in order that the children of Lêr might sustain no harm, they made a law that no man should injure a swan, from that time forth forever. They also instituted a yearly festival in their honor. But, after the children of Lêr had to leave Lake Darvra for the Sea of Moyle, they suffered greatly from cold and tempests. They were also very lonely, for only once during the three hundred years did an embassy from the people of the goddess Danu reach them and tell them all that had happened in Erin during their exile. Their long suffering came to an end only after their third stage in Irros Downaun and the Isle of Glora. Then they were free to return to their father's palace. But it was lonely and deserted, for Lêr had been killed by Cweeltya, a cousin of Finn MacCoul. So they wandered back to the Isle of Glora, where they found a friend in the Lonely Crane of Inniskea, who has lived there since the world began, and will be there when it ends. An attempt to Christianize the pagan story was made by the early monks, and we are told that the swans had a prevision of their disenchantment when Patrick would come to Erin to end the power of the gods forever. One day St. Kemoc, a disciple of Patrick, who had heard of their sufferings and pitied them, came to Glora. He brought them to his church, preached the new faith to them, and baptized them. This broke the pagan spell, and, as soon as the holy water was sprinkled over them, they returned to human shape. But they were very aged and bowed—three ancient men and one ancient woman. They did not long survive their baptism, and the saint buried them all together in one grave.

Luh Lavada, "Luh the Long-handed." He was the Irish sun-god and the crowning glory of the Gaelic Pantheon. He was the son of Kian, the son of Dianket, who was the god of medicine, and of Ayniu, daughter of Balor the Fomor. It was not with the bow

like the Greek Apollo, but with the rod-sling that the god did his
wonders. His worshipers sometimes saw the terrible weapon
in the sky as a rainbow, and the Milky Way was called "Luh's
Chain." He had a magic spear which he had not to wield himself;
for it was alive, and was so thirsty of blood that the only way to
keep it quiet was to steep its head in a decoction of poppy. When
it scented a battle, it roared and struggled against its thongs; fire
flashed from it, and, once free, it rushed through the ranks of the
enemy, never weary of slaughter. He had also a magic hound which,
according to a poem attributed to Cweeltya, the cousin of Finn
MacCoul, was irresistible in combat, and changed into mead or
wine the spring water in which it bathed. The spear and hound
were part of the blood-fine Luh had exacted from the sons of
Tuirenn for the murder of his father Kian. Luh gained his title
of Ildana, or "Master of All Arts," on his first visit to Nuada of the
Silver Hand, who was then king of the gods, at Tara. Nuada tested
him in all branches of knowledge, and found that he was master
of them all. Then he sent his best chess-player, who had defeated
all the gods at the game, to play with him. But Luh won, inventing
a new move, still known as "Luh's enclosure." Whereupon he was
invited to the palace and placed in the "sage's seat," reserved for
the wisest. Next he was requested to play the harp before the
assembled deities. So he played the sleep-tune, and they all fell
asleep, and did not wake until the same hour the following day.
Next, he played a plaintive air, and they all wept. Lastly, he played
a measure that sent them all into transports of joy. Then Nuada
thought that one so clever would be a great help to the gods against
the Fomors, and he lent his throne to Luh for thirteen days, taking
the "sage's seat" at his side. A council of the gods decided that
Luh's life was too valuable to be exposed to danger, and in the
pitched battle that ensued, he was left in the rear, guarded by nine
warriors. But Luh escaped from his wardens, and appeared in
his chariot before the army. And he drove around the ranks, so
that all the Tuaha dé Danauns might see him. The Fomors
saw him, too. "It is a wonder to me," said their commander to
his druids, "that the sun should rise in the west to-day, and in the
east every other day." "It would be better for us if it were so,"
replied the druids. "But what you see is the radiance of the face
of Luh of the Long Arms." Then the sun-god shouted a challenge

to his grandfather, Balor of the Mighty Blows, who was raging fiercely among the gods. With a magic stone he struck out Balor's eye, and the blinding of the Fomorian god won the victory for the people of the goddess Danu, and the Fomorians were driven back headlong to their country under the sea. Luh figures also as a solar deity of the ancient Britons, under the name of Lleu, and of Gaul, under that of Lugu. Three cities, Laon, Leyden, and Lyons—all anciently Lugdunum (Lugu's town)—were named after him, and at the last and greatest of these a festival was still held in Roman times upon the sun-god's day, the first of August, which corresponded to the Luhnassad (Luh's commemoration), held in ancient Ireland. Numerous stories about Luh's adventures are still current among the Irish peasantry.

Manannan. He was the greatest and most popular of the many children of Lêr, the god of the sea, and far more famous than his father. He was the protector of sailors especially, who invoked him as "God of Headlands," and of merchants, who claimed him as the first of the merchant class. His favorite dwelling-places were the Isle of Man, to which he gave his name, and Arran Island in the Firth of Clyde, where he had a palace called "Evaun of the Apple-trees." His weapons were famous: Two spears named "Yellow Shaft" and "Red Javelin," the "Retaliator," a sword that never failed to slay, as well as two others known as the "Great Fury" and the "Little Fury." He had a boat called "Wave-sweeper," which went with lightning speed wherever its owner desired, and required neither oar nor sail. His horse, "Splendid Mane," was fleeter than the spring wind, and traveled with equal speed on land and over the waves of the ocean. He was protected by his magic mail and breastplate, which no weapon could pierce, and the two magic jewels on his helmet blinded those who gazed on them too long. He endowed the gods with the mantle which rendered them invisible, and he fed them with his magic pigs which, like the boar Saehrimnir in the Norse Valhalla, renewed themselves after being eaten. Of these, too, he made his "Feast of Age," at which those who ate never grew old. In this way he kept the people of the goddess Danu eternally young. When the latter were defeated by the Milesians, a part of them, under the leadership of Manannan, decided to seek refuge in the paradise at the bottom of the sea off the west coast of Erin. It is a deep-meadowed, happy land of perpetual summer and pleasure. The name by which it is chiefly known is Tir-nan-ōg, "The Land of Youth." It sometimes rises to the surface of the Atlantic, and a patient watcher, after much gazing, may catch a glimpse of it from the westernmost coasts of Ireland or Scotland against the sunset. But he almost invariably goes mad afterward from longing. Manannan and his wife Fand were at once acknowledged King and Queen of this Celtic Elysium. But the god frequently visits his former haunts, and, when an aged Highlander sees a tall, beautiful stranger, with a crest on his head, enter his shieling, and tell him many strange things, he knows he has been conversing with the Son of the Sea. He was the special guardian of Irishmen in foreign lands, assisting them in their perils, and bringing them home safe. He is by no means forgotten in the Isle of Man, of which tradition states he was the first inhabitant. He was also its first king, and kept it safe from invasion by his magic. For he would cause mists to arise and hide the island, or he would make one man seem to be a hundred, or he would fling little chips of wood into the water, and they would appear to the enemy to be great war vessels. So he held his kingdom against all comers, until his power, like that of the other Gaelic gods, came to an end. A legend, believed by patriotic Manxmen, is that he had three legs, upon which he used to travel at a great pace. How this was done may be seen from the arms of the island, on which are pictured his three limbs, joined together, and spread out like the spokes of a wheel.

PART IX

NORTH AMERICAN INDIAN

The Boy that Set a Snare for the Sun. At the time when the animals reigned in the earth, they had killed all the people but a girl and her little brother, and these two were living in fear, in an out-of-the-way place. The boy was a pygmy, not larger than an infant; but the girl had grown naturally, so that the care of providing food and shelter fell wholly upon her. She went out every day to get wood for the lodge-fire, and took her little brother in order that no mishap should fall upon him. A big bird that was mischievous might have flown away with him. She made him a bow and arrows, and said to him one day: "My little brother, I will leave you behind where I have been gathering the wood; you must hide yourself, and you will soon see the snow-birds come and pick up the worms out of the logs which I have piled up. Shoot one of them and bring it home."

He obeyed her, and tried his best to kill one, but he came home unsuccessful. His sister told him that he must not despair, but try again the next day. She accordingly left him at the gathering-place of the wood, and returned to the lodge. Toward nightfall she heard his little footsteps crackling through the snow, and he hurried in and threw down, with an air of triumph, one of the birds which he had killed. "My sister," said he, "I wish you to skin it and stretch the skin, and when I have killed more I will have a coat made out of them."

"But what shall we do with the body?" said she, for they had always lived upon greens and berries. "Cut it in two," he answered, "and season our pottage with one-half of it at a time." She did so, and they relished it greatly.

The boy kept on in his efforts, and in the course of time he had killed ten birds, out of the skins of which his sister made him a little coat. It was a very pretty little coat, and he had one skin to spare.

341

"Sister," said he one day, as he paraded up and down before
the lodge, enjoying his new coat and fancying himself the greatest
little fellow in the world, as he was, for there was no other, he said:
"My sister, are we really alone in the world, or are we playing at
it? Is there nobody else living? And tell me, was all this great
broad earth and this huge big sky made for a little boy and girl like
you and me?"

"By no means," she answered. "There were many folk very
unlike a harmless girl and boy, who lived in another part of the
earth and had killed all their kinsfolk;" and she told him that if he
would live blameless and not endanger his life, he must never go
where they were. This only served to inflame the boy's curiosity;
and he soon after took his bow and arrows and went in that direction.
After walking a long time and meeting no one, he became tired and
stretched himself upon a high green knoll where the day's warmth
had melted off the snow. It was a charming place to lie upon, and
he fell asleep; and the sun beat so hot upon him that it not only
singed his bird-skin coat, but it so shriveled and shrunk and tight-
ened it upon the little boy's body, as to wake him up. When he felt
how the sun had served his coat, and what mischief it had played
with the garment he was so proud of, he flew into a great passion and
berated the sun in a way really terrible for a boy no higher than a
man's knee; and he vowed fearful things against it. "Do you
think you are too high?" said he. "I shall revenge myself. Oh, sun,
I will have you yet for a plaything."

On coming home he gave his sister an account of his misfortune,
and bitterly bewailed the spoiling of his new coat. He would not
eat so much as a single berry. For ten days he lay on his bed without
so much as turning over, despite his sister's entreaties, and at the
end of that time he turned and lay for ten days longer on the other
side. When he got up he was very pale, but very resolute. He
bade his sister make him a snare, because, as he told her, he meant
to catch the sun. At first she thought she had nothing with which
to form it; but at last she brought out a deer's sinew, which her
father had left, and she made it into a string suitable for a noose.
But the little brother was quite angry and said that would not do,
she must find something else. "I have nothing at all," said she,
but she next produced the bird-skin that was left over when the coat
was made, and she wrought that into a string, but the little boy was

more wroth than before. "The sun has had enough of my bird-skins," said he; "find something else." She went out of the lodge, saying to herself: "Was there ever so obstinate a boy?" She did not dare say this time that she had nothing, and, luckily, she thought of her own beautiful hair, and taking a lock of it she braided it into a cord and, returning, handed it to her brother. The moment his eye fell upon that jet-black braid he was delighted, and ran it back and forth through his hands as swiftly as he could, and as he drew it forth he tried its strength. "This will do," he said, and winding it in a glossy coil about his shoulders, he set out from the lodge a little after midnight. His object was to catch the sun before he rose. He fixed his snare firmly on a spot just where the sun must strike the land as it rose above the earth; and sure enough, he caught the sun so that it was held fast by the cord and did not rise.

The animals that ruled the earth were immediately put into great commotion. They had no light, and they ran to and fro, calling out to one another and asking what had happened. They summoned a council to debate upon the matter, and an old dormouse, suspecting where the trouble lay, proposed that someone should be appointed to go and cut the cord. This was a bold thing to undertake, as the rays of the sun could not fail to burn whoever should venture so near to them. At last the venerable dormouse himself undertook it, for the very good reason that nobody else would. At this time the dormouse was the largest animal in the world. When he stood up he looked like a mountain. It made haste to the place where the sun lay ensnared; and as it came nearer and nearer, its back began to smoke and burn with the heat, and the whole top of its huge bulk was turned in a very short time to enormous heaps of ashes. It succeeded, however, in cutting the cord with its teeth and freeing the sun, which rolled up again as round and beautiful as ever, into the wide, blue sky. But the dormouse, or blind woman, as it is called, was shrunk away into a very small size, and that is the reason why it is now one of the tiniest creatures on earth.

The little boy returned home when he found that the sun had escaped his snare, and devoted himself entirely to hunting. "If the beautiful hair of my sister would not hold the sun fast, nothing else could," said he. "I am not born, a little fellow like me, to look after the sun," said he. "It requires some one greater and wiser than I am to look after that." And he went out and shot ten more snow-birds; for he had become very expert in this business, and he had a new bird-skin coat made, which was even prettier than the one he had worn before.

The Celestial Sisters. Waupee, the White Hawk, lived in a remote part of the forest, where animals abounded. Every day he returned from the chase with a large spoil, for he was one of the most skilful and lucky hunters of his tribe. His form was like the cedar; the fire of youth was in his eye; there was no forest too gloomy for him to penetrate, and no track made by bird or beast that he could not follow. One day he had gone beyond any point that he had ever visited before. He traveled through an open wood where he had a long, clear vista. He saw a light breaking through the foliage of the distant trees which made him feel sure that he was nearing a prairie. He reached a wide plain, covered with long grass and flowers. After walking through the pathless plain for some time he came to a place where there was a ring in the grass, as if it had been made by footsteps moving lightly round and round. But it was so strange that the hawk paused and looked at it in wonder. There was no path that led to the circle. Not even a crushed leaf or a broken twig was to be seen on any side, certainly no trace of footsteps could have been found. Presently he heard faint sounds of music in the air, and as the magic notes died away he saw a small object like a summer cloud floating down from above. At first it was very small, and seemed likely to be blown away on the first breeze that swept by, but it grew and the music came nearer, and fell more sweetly on the ear. When it reached the earth it took the form of a basket which was filled with twelve maidens of lovely form and enchanting faces. As soon as the basket touched the ground they leaped out and danced joyously around the ring, striking now and then a shining ball which gave out ravishing melody. White Hawk was entranced, but the youngest of the sisters captured most of his admiration, and he rushed forward with the thought of expressing his delight. As he did so, the sisters, with the quickness of birds terrified at the sight of man, leaped into their basket and were drawn into the sky.

Poor Waupee gazed longingly after the retreating sisters, sighing aloud, "They are gone. I shall see them no more." He went back to his lonely covert, but he could not rest. The sky possessed the only being whom he had loved. The next day, at the same hour,

with soft cushions of dry moss. One of the sisters kept the house tidy and the food cooked while the other nursed Gray Eagle and turned his pillows when he was tired of one position. The brother was the physician, and when his duties were done he sought such game as was to be found in cold weather—and so was always busy, killing or curing. On his hunting excursions Dr. Falcon carried the youngest, who was a foolish little fellow.

In due time, with good nursing and good air, Gray Eagle recovered from his wound, and he was able, by spring, to replenish the larder and teach the family. They were all successful except Peepi, the youngest. Being small and foolish and feather-headed, he often came home with an empty game bag and his feathers terribly ruffled. In answer to Gray Eagle's questions he replied that his ill-luck was not from his smallness nor weakness. That he killed ducks every time he went out, but that Ko-ko-ho robbed him of it. The next day Gray Eagle seated himself to watch.

Peepi pounced upon a duck and was bringing it to land when Ko-ko-ho, the White Owl, attacked him, and claimed his prey. Gray Eagle fixed his talons in Ko-ko-ho, and flew away with him to their nest. Arrived there, with his duck, Peepi was for flying in the White Owl's face and putting his eyes out.

"Softly, Peepi," said Gray Eagle; "don't be in such a huff, my little brother. Do you not know we should forgive our enemies? White Owl may go, but let this be a lesson to him not to play the tyrant."

The Two Jeebi. In the north lived a hunter who had a wife and one child. His lodge stood far off in the forest, several days' journey from any other. He spent his days in hunting, and his evenings in relating to his wife the incidents that had befallen him. As game was very abundant, he found no difficulty in killing as much as they wanted. Just in all his acts, he lived a peaceful and happy life.

One evening during the winter season, it chanced that he remained out longer than usual, and his wife began to fear that some accident had befallen him. It was already dark. She listened attentively, and at last heard the sound of approaching footsteps. Not doubting that it was her husband, she went to the door and beheld two strange women. She bade them enter, and invited them to remain. She saw that they were total strangers in the country. There was something so peculiar in their looks, air, and manner that she felt disturbed. They would not come near the fire. They sat in a remote part of the lodge, shy and taciturn, and drew their garments about them in such a way as nearly to hide their faces. So far as she could judge, they were pale, hollow-eyed, and long-visaged, very thin and emaciated.

There was but little light in the lodge, as the fire was low, and its fitful flashes, by disclosing their white faces and then dropping them suddenly into darkness, served rather to increase than to dispel her fears.

"Merciful Spirit!" cried a voice from the opposite part of the lodge; "there are two corpses clothed with garments."

The hunter's wife turned around, but, seeing nobody, save her little child, staring across from under his blanket, she said to herself: "The boy cannot speak; the sounds were but the gusts of wind." She trembled and was ready to sink to the earth. Her husband at this moment entered, and in some measure relieved her alarm. He threw down the carcass of a large, fat deer.

"Behold, what a fine and fat animal!" cried the mysterious women; and they immediately ran and pulled off pieces of the whitest fat, which they greedily devoured. The hunter and his wife looked on with astonishment, but remained silent. They supposed that their guests might have been stricken with famine. The next day, however, the same unusual conduct was repeated. The strange women again tore off the fat and devoured it with eagerness. The third day the hunter thought that he would anticipate their wants by tying up a share of the hunt, and setting it aside for their express use. They accepted it, but still appeared dissatisfied, and went to the wife's portion and tore off more. The hunter and his wife were surprised at such rude and unaccountable conduct, but they remained silent, for they respected their guests, and had observed that they had been attended with marked good luck during the sojourn of these mysterious visitors in their lodge.

In other respects, the deportment of the women was strictly unexceptionable. They were modest, distant, and silent. They never uttered a word during the day. At night they occupied themselves in procuring wood, which they carried to the lodge, and then, restoring the implements exactly where they had found them, resumed their places without speaking. They were never known to stay out until daylight. They never laughed or jested.

The winter was nearly passed away, when, one evening, the hunter was abroad later than usual. The moment he came in and laid down his day's hunt, as was his custom, before his wife, the two women seized upon the deer and began to tear off the fat in so unceremonious a way that her anger was excited. She restrained herself, however, in a good degree, but could not wholly conceal her feelings, though she said but little.

The strange guests observed the state of her mind, and they became uneasy, and withdrew farther still into the remote gloom of the lodge. The good hunter saw the eclipse that was darkening the quiet of his lodge, and carefully inquired of its cause; but his wife denied having used any words of complaining or reproach. They retired to their couches, and the hunter tried to compose himself to sleep, but could not, for the sighs and sobs of the two women were incessant.

"Tell me," said he, "what is it that gives you pain of mind? Has my wife given you offense?"

"No," they answered. "We have been treated with kindness and affection. But our mission is not to you only. We come from the other land to test mankind, and to try the sincerity of the living. We have heard the bereaved by death say that if the lost could be restored, they would devote their lives to them and make them happy. We are your two dead sisters. Three moons were allotted us by the Master of Life to make the trial. More than half the time had been successfully passed when the angry feelings of your wife indicated the irksomeness you felt at our presence, and has made us resolve to depart. You have thought our conduct rude in possessing ourselves of the best part of the hunt. That was the point of trial selected to put you to. It is the wife's peculiar privilege. You love your wife. For another to usurp what belongs to her we know to be the severest test of her goodness of heart, and thus of your temper and feelings. Pardon us. We are the agents of him who sent us. Peace to your dwelling. Farewell."

When they ceased total darkness filled the lodge. The two spirits were seen no more, but success attended the hunter, as they had promised.

Leelinau, the Lost Daughter. Leelinau was the favorite daughter of a hunter, who lived on the lake shore near the base of the lofty highlands, called Kang Wudjoo. From her earliest youth she was seen to be thoughtful and retiring. She was much alone, and seemed to enjoy the society of her own shadow better than that of the lodge circle. Her attachment to Manitowok, the fairy wood, was so engrossing that her parents feared some evil spirit had enticed her to its haunts and cast a charm upon her. This belief was confirmed when, one day, her mother, who had secretly followed her, heard her murmuring to some invisible companion words like these: "Spirit of the dancing leaves, hear a throbbing heart in its sadness. Spirit of the foaming stream, visit my nightly pillow. Spirit of the starry night, lead my footprints to the blushing Mis-kodeed. Spirit of the greenwood plume, shed on me thy leafy fra-grance."

The time of the corn-gathering came, and the young people assembled to pluck it. One of the girls had found a red ear, and all congratulated her that a brave admirer was on his way to her father's lodge. Presently it chanced that one of the young men espied in Leelinau's hands a crooked ear, and at once the term Wa-ge-nine was shouted, and the whole field was in a roar.

"The thief is in the corn-field!" said the youth. "See you not the old man stooping as he enters?" He accompanied this with the action of one bowed with age, stealing into the corn-field.

"Leelinau, the old man is thine!" he exclaimed.

The next morning the eldest son of a neighboring chief called at her father's lodge. He was quite advanced in years, but he had won such renown as warrior and hunter that the parents accepted him as suitor for their daughter; but Leelinau steadily declined his attentions, while her parents, believing her shy, set the day for the wedding. She stole away to her greenwood, and presently a sound, at first like a sigh, grew to these words:

"Maiden, think me not a tree. I am thine own dear lover.

> "Come, and on the mountain free,
> Rove a fairy bright with me."

Leelinau heard the magical words, and resolved that no warrior's son should clasp her hand. On the eve of her wedding-day she decked herself in her best garments and maiden ornaments and said to her parents:

"I am going to meet my little lover, the chieftain of the Green Plume, who is waiting for me at the Spirit Grove."

Hour chased hour as the clouds of evening rolled up in the west; darkness came on, but no daughter returned. The wood was searched with torches, but in vain. Leelinau was nowhere to be seen. Nevermore did she visit her home. The fisherman, who went seldom to the lonely lake, reported seeing a woman's figure on the shore, which seemed to flee as their light skiff approached, and waving over its head they thought that they beheld the green plumes of a fairy lover.

Manabozho, the Mischief-Maker. There was never in the whole world a more mischievous busybody than that notorious giant, Manabozho. He was everywhere, in season and out of season, running about and putting his hand into whatever was going forward. He could take almost any shape he pleased; he could be very wise or very foolish, very weak or very strong, very poor or very rich—as happened to suit his humor. Whatever anyone else could do he would attempt without a moment's hesitation. He was a match for any man he met, and there were few manitos that could get the better of him. He would be very kind or very cruel; an animal or a bird; a man or a spirit; and yet, in spite of all these gifts, Manabozho was always getting himself involved in all sorts of troubles; and more than once he was driven to his wits' end to come off with his life. While yet a youngster, living with his grandmother on the edge of the prairie, he was taught by her to take a deep interest in every sight and sound, and he was often very much frightened at what he heard and saw, and his grandmother laughed at his fears, but told him their source.

One day he began such a loud lamentation that it shook the lodge, and his grandmother asked him what was the matter. Manabozho started off again with his doleful hubbub, but managed to jerk out the words, between his sobs, "I haven't got any father nor mother; I haven't," and he became more boisterous in his cries than ever. Knowing that he was of a wicked and revengeful disposition, his grandmother dreaded to tell him the story of his parentage. At last she said:

"Yes, you have a father and three brothers living. Your mother is dead. She was taken for a wife by your father, the West, without the consent of her parents. Your brothers are the North, East, and South; and, being older than you, your father has given them great power with the winds."

"I am glad my father is living," said Manabozho. "I shall set out to-morrow to visit him." He had now grown to such size that he had to live out of doors, and if he had cared to he could have snapped off the heads of birds nesting in the tallest trees, as he walked along, and pulled one of them up by the roots for a staff. He found his father far up near the clouds on a mountain-top, and they spent some days talking to each other, for they were so huge that it took a whole day for either of them to express a single idea, it was so immense. One evening Manabozho asked his father what he was most afraid of on earth, and he replied: "Nothing."

"But is there nothing that could hurt you?" he asked.

"Yes," said his father, "there is a black stone a hundred miles from here. If it should happen to hit me, it would hurt me very much. Now, tell no one that the black stone is bad medicine for your father," he added. "Is there not something that you do not like?"

"Nothing," replied the son; but after being urged seventeen times he said:

"Jee-jee, jee-jee! Yoe! Yoe! I cannot name it, I tremble so."

The West told him to banish his fears and speak plainly, and Manabozho would have gone through the same make-believe, if his father had not threatened to pitch him into a river that was five miles off.

"Father," said he, "since you will know, it is the root of the bulrush."

After a while Manabozho said: "I will get a little of the black rock to see how it looks."

"And I," said the West, "will get a little of the root of the bulrush and see how it tastes."

As they were each trying to deceive the other, they were ready for desperate work, and so when Manabozho strode two hundred miles for the black rock, the West hurried down the mountain on his quest. At daybreak they each appeared on the mountain-top. Manabozho had twenty loads at least of the black rock, and the West had a whole meadow of bulrush. Manabozho was first to strike, and when he threw a load of black rock he received in reply a shower of bulrush. When these weapons were gone they began hurling crags on the one hand and forest trees on the other, until, at last, Manabozho had pressed his father to the very edge of the world.

"Hold, my son," said the West; "I allow that I am fairly out of breath, but you cannot kill me. Pause where you are. Your brothers have the other quarters of the globe, but you can go and do a great deal of good to the people of earth, and when you have finished your work I will assign you a place."

When Manabozho's wounds were cured by his grandmother's medicine he was ripe for new adventures. He turned his thought toward Pearl Feather, a wicked old manito who had slain his grand-father. He made bows and arrows without number, but he had no heads for the shafts. Noko told him that an old man of whom she knew could furnish him, and he sent her to get some. She returned with her wrapper full, and he said that was not enough, she must go again, and she got as many more; but he had decided that he must learn how to make them.

"Noko," he said, "while I beat my drum do you go and get larger heads."

He fixed a great bird to his drum, so that it would continue to sound, and followed his grandmother without her knowledge. He watched the workman, and he also saw the old man's beautiful daughter, and he found that he had a heart, while the old man shivered and said, "How the wind blows!" as Manabozho uttered his first sigh of love. In the evening the grandmother said:

"You ought to fast before you go to war, to see whether you will be successful."

He consented, but privately he stored away two or three dozen juicy bears, a moose, and twenty strings of the tenderest birds. The place of his fast had been chosen by Noko, and she told him it must be so far as to be beyond the sound of her voice or it would be unlucky. This made him curious to know why she chose this spot, and so the next day he went but a short distance. "A little farther off!" she called out, and he came nearer, while pretending from the tone of his voice to be going farther away. He had not been long in ambush when an old magician crept into the lodge. They began talking about Manabozho, and he was convinced that they were kissing each other. Indignant at such a liberty taken toward his grandmother, he touched the magician's hair with a live coal that he had blown over, and the magician jumped high and ran blazing like a fire-ball across the prairie. Meanwhile Manabozho stole off to his fasting-place, and called out in heart-broken tones:

"Noko, is it time for me to come home?"

"Yes," she cried. "Did you see anything?" she asked, as he came.

"Nothing," he answered; and the next day he set out for the fiery serpents.

"You cannot pass," they said, and he turned his canoe as if to go back, when he called suddenly, "What is that behind you?" and when they turned to look he glided by them, and with his bow and arrow shot everyone, and next attacked the fortress of Pearl Feather, who appeared on the height, blazing like the sun. All day long the fight was kept up, and he was at his wits' end when a large woodpecker flew by and cried: "Shoot at the lock of hair on the crown of his head."

The first arrow only drew a few drops of blood, but the woodpecker's hint enabled him to lay the manito low, and, as a reward, he rubbed a drop of blood on the bird, so that his feathers might always remind of his good deed. He next tried his prowess as a fisherman, and captured a fish so large that with the oil be formed a small lake. He then invited all the birds and beasts, and as they arrived told them to plunge in and help themselves. By the time the hare and the martin appeared there was not a drop left, and they are, in consequence, the leanest of all creatures. He then played for them to dance, and as he sang and lulled them after their feast he helped himself to the creatures that had swallowed the most oil and so were fat and juicy. A small duck opened one eye and, seeing what Manabozho was doing, called out, "He is killing us," and sprang into the water. Manabozho was so vexed at him that he gave him a kick, and that is the reason the diver's tail-feathers are few, his back flattened, and his legs so straight that he makes a poor figure at walking.

Then Manabozho set out on a hunting excursion, and he met some wolf whelps, whose father had told them to beware of him.

"My grandchildren, where are you going?" he asked.

The old wolf advanced and said: "We are looking for good hunting-grounds to pass the winter in. What brings you here?"

"I was looking for you," said Manabozho. "I always admired your family; could you change me into a wolf?"

"Yes," replied the wolf, and he was immediately changed.

"Could you make my tail a little longer and more bushy?" he

all the indications of extreme old age. He again cast his eyes in the direction of the clouds, and uttered the peculiar cry which had given him the victory at the rock. In a moment the youth and beauty of his wife returned; her dingy garments assumed the shining appearance of green silk, and her staff was changed into a silver feather.

The lodge again shook and trembled, for they were now passing through the uppermost clouds, and they immediately afterward found themselves in the Evening Star, the residence of Osseo's father.

"My son," said the old man, "hang that cage of birds which you have in your hand at the door, and I will tell you why you and your wife have been sent for." Osseo obeyed and then took his seat in the lodge.

"Pity was shown to you," resumed the King of the Star, "on account of the contempt of your wife's sister, who laughed at her ill-fortune, and ridiculed you while you were under the power of the wicked spirit, whom you overcame at the rock. That spirit lives in the next lodge, being the small star you see on the left of mine, and he has always felt envious of my family because we had greater power, and especially that we had committed to us the care of the female world. He failed in many attempts to destroy your brothers and sisters-in-law, but succeeded at last in transforming yourself and your wife into decrepit old people. You must be careful and not let the light of his beams fall upon you while you are here, for therein lies the power of his enchantment. A ray of light is the bow and arrow he uses."

Osseo lived happy and contented in the parental lodge, and in due time his wife presented him with a son, who grew up rapidly and in the very likeness of Osseo himself. He was very quick and ready in learning everything that was done in his grandfather's dominions, but he wished also to learn the art of hunting, for he had heard that this was a favorite pastime below. To gratify him his father made him a bow and arrows, and he then let the birds out of the cage that he might practise in shooting. In this pastime he soon became expert, and the very first day he brought down a bird; but when he went to pick it up, to his amazement it was a beautiful young woman, with the arrow sticking in her breast. It was one of his younger aunts. The moment her blood fell upon the surface of that pure and spotless planet, the charm was dissolved. The boy immediately found himself sinking, although he was partly upheld by something like wings until he passed through the lower clouds, and he then suddenly dropped upon a high, breezy island in a large lake. He was pleased to see all his aunts and uncles following him in the form of birds, and he soon discovered the silver lodge, with his father and mother, descending with its waving tassels fluttering like so many insects' gilded wings. It rested on the loftiest cliffs of the island, and there they fixed their residence. They all resumed their natural shapes, but they were diminished to the size of fairies; and as a mark of homage to the King of the Evening Star, they never failed on every pleasant evening during the summers to join hands and dance upon the top of the rocks, and Osseo and his wife, as fondly attached as ever, always led the dance.

The Red Swan. Three brothers were left destitute at an early age by the death of their parents, and they had no neighbors to lend them a helping hand. The eldest became expert in forest craft and successful in procuring food, but when the younger ones were able to care for themselves, and the eldest proposed to go in search of the world, the others objected so much that he abandoned the thought and arranged that each should kill the animal he was most expert in shooting, and make quivers of their skins, for they all had a presentiment that something requiring arrows was about to happen. They set out on their different paths. Maidwa, the youngest, had not gone far when he saw a bear, an animal which, by the agreement, he was not to kill; he nevertheless sent an arrow through him and began to skin him. Immediately something red tinged all the air about him. As he stood wondering, a strange noise came to his ear, and following the sound he reached the shore of a lake upon whose waters floated a most beautiful red swan. Drawing his arrow to his ear, he discharged the shaft, but it took no effect. He shot again and again till his quiver was empty, but the swan remained as before. He ran to the lodge and brought every arrow, but in vain. Then he remembered that in his father's medicine sack were three magic arrows, and he hurried for them. With trembling hand he shot at the glorious bird. The first shot grazed the wing, the second cut a few bright feathers, and the third passed through the beautiful throat. But when he cried, "The bird is mine!" and looked to see it fall and drift ashore, he beheld it rise majestically and sail toward the sunset. He rescued two of the magic arrows, and then started in pursuit of the swan. He could run so fast that an arrow which he had shot would fall behind him, and in due time he reached a village where a watchman proclaimed his approach and directed him to the lodge of the chief, who immediately set him beside his daughter, whom he ordered to see if the stranger's moccasins were torn, and to bring in his bundle. It was some time before she moved to do so, and then he snatched them from her hand and hung them up. He wakened early, and finding the chief's daughter at the door he asked her what time the swan passed, saying: "I am following it; come out and point the way."

He passed the day in running, and he thought that he discerned its faint red light in the west. When night came he had entered another village, and was again treated kindly by the chieftain and by a more beautiful daughter. Before daybreak he again asked about the swan, and learned from the maiden when it passed and in what direction. After dark on the third day he saw a light shining from a small lodge in which was an old man alone. Without turning his eyes the old man said: "Walk in, my grandchild." He spoke about it and immediately a kettle with legs appeared on the fire. When it had boiled the old man said, "It will stand at a distance," and the kettle removed itself and Maidwa helped himself while the pot remained as full as before.

The next morning the old man gave him his blessing as he set out on his quest, and that night he again found himself in company of an old man who received him kindly, and whose frisky little kettle hurried about without being spoken of. The next day he traveled with a light heart, and at nightfall entered the lodge of still another old man whose kettle, in coming and going, sang little songs or made a remark now and then.

"Young man," said the old warrior, "the errand you are bound on is beset with difficulties. This red swan you are following is the daughter of a magician who has abundance of everything, but only this one child, whom he values more than the sacred arrows. In former times he wore a cap of wampum, which was attached to his scalp; but powerful Indians told him that their chief's daughter was on the brink of the grave, and that she had asked for the wampum cap because she believed it would save her life. The magician at last parted with it, although when he handed it to the bearers it left the crown of his head bare and bloody. This was all a cheat, and the magician has since been the sport of all. The wampum scalp is danced from village to village, and the crown of the head where it lay has never healed. Many have sacrificed themselves to recover it, but they never have succeeded. The red swan has enticed you to try, as she has many another. When you near the magician's lodge you will hear groans, and he will speed you on your way when he learns your errand."

Toward the next evening Maidwa heard groans proceeding from a distant lodge, and, entering, saw a man with a bare and bloody crown.

"Sit down," said he; "we will have something to eat."

"In a moment," said the kettle from the corner.

"You will oblige me by making all the despatch you can," said the magician, in a very humble tone, addressing the kettle.

"Have patience," replied the kettle; "I will be with you presently."

After a time a great kettle advanced in a stately manner in front of the magician. "What shall we have, sir?" it said.

"Corn, if you please," he answered.

"No, we will have whortleberries," said the kettle.

"Very well, just as you choose," he answered.

"Hold a minute!" said the kettle, as Maidwa was about to help himself in response to an invitation from his host. After some delay the kettle said: "Now we are ready."

"Will the kettle withdraw?" asked the magician.

"No, we will stay a little longer and hear what the young man says," it replied.

"Very well," he answered, and, turning to Maidwa, he said: "You see my predicament. I have to take counsel with my kettle, or I should be alone and without food."

Maidwa now and then heard a rustling behind a curtain that stirred his heart in a strange way. Maidwa listened while between groans the old man asked him about his dreams and his guardian spirit.

"Keep cool," said the kettle.

"Have you no dreams of another kind?" he was asked.

"Yes," said he, and the kettle said: "We are much pleased with that."

"Yes, yes, you will cause me to live," said the magician. "Will you go in search of my scalp?"

"Yes," said Maidwa, "and day after to-morrow when the ka-kak cries you will know that I am successful."

The next afternoon, in a wood, Maidwa heard the shouts of many persons, and on coming to the plain he saw that their heads appeared like hanging leaves, there were so many. On a post was waving the wampum scalp, and a war-dance was being danced about it. Maidwa changed himself into a humming-bird, and flew toward the scalp. As he neared it he changed himself into the down that floats in air, and sailed upon the scalp. He loosened it, and a lucky current of air bore it up as he moved off with it. The dancers stopped in such amaze that the good wind, increasing, bore it beyond their reach. Then he changed into a hawk, and flew off swiftly with his trophy, crying "ka-kak!" till the shrill tones resounded through the land. As Maidwa, the hawk, restored the scalp to the magician's head, and entered the lodge in his own person, what was his delight to see a bright and cheerful youth replace the aged form.

Although Maidwa's heart was burning to see the red swan, or hear her spoken of, he restrained himself, and finally prepared his bundle for a homeward journey. But ere he was ready the curtain of the lodge parted and a beautiful young woman appeared, so majestic and airy that she seemed to belong in the free heaven rather than in that dusky lodge. "Take her," said the magician, "for you are worthy. She is ready to go with you to your home and kindred, and has been ever since you came."

Robin Redbreast. An old man had an only son, named Iadilla, who had reached the age when it is thought proper to make the long and final fast which is to secure through life a guardian genius or spirit. The father was ambitious that his son should surpass all others in whatever was deemed wisest and greatest among his people. To accomplish this he thought it necessary that Iadilla's fast should be made longer than any of those whose fame he coveted for his son. After the son had been several times in the sweating-lodge and bath, which were to prepare and purify him for communion with his good spirit, he was told to lie down on a clean mat in a little lodge expressly made for him. His father enjoined him to bear his fast like a man, and promised that at the expiration of twelve days he should receive food and the father's blessing. The lad carefully observed the command, and lay with his face covered, waiting the approach of the spirit that was to decide his good or evil fortune.

Each morning the father came to his lodge door with words of encouragement, but to his glowing promises the son made no reply, but lay without discontent or murmur until the ninth day. Then he said to his father:

"My dreams forbode evil. May I break my fast now, and make a new at a more favorable time?"

The father answered: "My son, you know not what you ask. If you rise now, all your glory will depart. Wait patiently a little longer."

The son assented, and lay until the eleventh day, when he repeated the request. The father renewed his promise and entreaty, saying:

"Will you bring shame upon your father when his sun is sinking in the west?"

"I will not shame you, my father," said Iadilla, and lay so still that only by a gentle heaving of his breast could you know that he lived.

At the dawn of the next morning the father prepared a great repast for his son, and hastened to set it before him. On coming to the door of the little lodge he was surprised to hear his son talking to himself. He was yet more astonished when he saw that he was painted with vermilion all over his breast, and was in the act of finishing his work by painting as far back on his shoulders as he could reach, saying, as he did so:

"My father has destroyed my fortune as a man. He would not listen to my requests. He has urged me beyond my tender strength. He will be the loser. I shall be forever happy in my new state, for I have been obedient to my parent. He alone will be the sufferer, for my guardian spirit is a just one. Though not propitious to me in the manner I desired, he has shown me pity in another way— he has given me another shape; and now I must go."

The old man broke into the lodge, exclaiming: "My son, leave me not, I pray you."

But the young man, with the quickness of a bird, had flown to the top of the lodge and perched himself on the highest pole, having been changed into a beautiful robin redbreast. He looked down upon his father with pity beaming in his eyes, and said:

"Regret not, my father, the change you behold. I shall be happier in my present state than I could have been as a man. I shall always be the friend of men, and keep near their dwellings. I shall ever be contented and happy; and although I could not gratify your wishes as a warrior, it will be my daily aim to make you amends for it as a harbinger of peace and joy. I will cheer you by my songs, and try to inspire such joy in others as I feel myself."

Then stretching himself as if he gloried in his gift of wings, Iadilla caroled one of his sweetest songs and flew away to the neighboring greenwood.

Sheem. On a certain afternoon the sun was falling in the west, and it fell upon a solitary lodge on the banks of a lonely lake. The wife and children of a dying man were gathered about his buffalo robe. Of the children, a son and daughter were nearly grown, and the other was a mere child. The dying father charged them on no account to forsake the little brother, however much they might be tempted to return to a world which he had left in order to enjoy peace with poverty rather than plenty with warfare and sorrow. The mother soon followed the father to the spirit world. The girl, being the eldest, directed her brothers, and seemed to be tender and affectionate toward the youngest, who was slight in frame and of strange nature. The old boy soon became restless, and said:

"Sister, are we never to live like other human beings in the world? Must I never mingle with my kind? I am resolved to seek a village, and you cannot prevent me."

"I do not say no to your desires, brother," said she, "but we are to cherish each other, and our young brother, who is a weakling, is entitled to a double share of our love."

The youth listened in silence, and he devoted himself to the little home. The brothers often played together and one day the ball they threw was not once allowed to touch the ground, so deft were they. A wicked manito inhabited the lake by which they played, and he resolved to make the elder hit the ball sideways so that it should fall into his canoe and give him power over the thrower. When Owasso saw the old man he professed to be much surprised, as was, in truth, little Sheem, the younger.

"Bring us the ball!" they both cried out.

"Come and get your ball," said the manito.

Owasso ran into the water and held out his hand.

"Reach it yourself," said the manito, and as he reached the magician pulled him into the canoe.

"Take my little brother, too, grandfather," said Owasso. "He will starve if I leave him."

Mishosha only laughed, and his canoe glided through the water like an arrow. The two daughters of Mishosha were seated in the lodge when they arrived. He said to the eldest, "I have brought you a husband, my daughter," and the young woman smiled, for he was comely to look upon.

But no sooner was Owasso in the family than the manito wished him out of the way. He said to him one day, "You can go fishing with me," and they started without delay, for at the magician's voice the canoe moved. The manito advised Owasso to spear a large sturgeon which came along, and with glassy eye seemed to recognize the magician. Owasso rose in the boat to spear it, when the magician darted forward with such violence as to hurl him into the water while the canoe carried the manito out of sight. Owasso had magical powers and he ordered the fish to swim ashore with him, which he did, and the manito, on reaching home, was very uneasy at being thus outwitted, so he again asked Owasso to accompany him, and he was carried to crags covered with gulls.

"Go on shore, my son, and pick up some gull's eggs," he said, and again he shot away, leaving the youth in peril.

But Owasso uttered a charm and the gulls flew around him in vast numbers, and he told them to fly close together so that he could ride home on their backs. In this way he again reached home first. The next journey was to an eagle's nest in the top of a tall tree—a tree that grew taller and taller as he climbed.

"Listen, eagles," said the manito. "You have long expected a gift from me. I present you with this boy, who has had the presumption to climb up and disturb your nest," and again he was left to his fate, and again he was borne on great wings swiftly through the air, and stood ready to greet his father-in-law at home.

It happened one evening while the manito was pondering on his last charm that Owasso and his wife wandered to the lake and sat beside it, and the breeze wafted a song to their ears that gave Owasso great distress.

"It is the voice of Sheem!" he cried, "of my little brother. Oh, if I could only see him!"

the hunter found the remains of his wife strewn on the ground. He built another lodge, and, gathering his wife's bones, placed them in the hollow of a tree that grew near.

As time went on, while the father was hunting, the child amused himself by shooting arrows which his father had made for him, but search as he might, he could never find them. At last he bethought himself of the arrows left to him by the good Weendigoe, and he shot one of those from his bow. It struck against the hollow tree where his father had deposited the mother's bones. When he ran to find the arrow the face of a beautiful boy peeped out from the tree. The lonely little lad asked the boy to come out and play with him, and having secured a promise that he would not let the father know, the boy sprang from the tree and they played joyously all day. They shot their arrows by turns, when, suddenly, the visitor said, "Your father is coming. We must stop," and he disappeared into the tree.

When the hunter arrived his son sat demurely by the fire, and in the course of the evening he asked his father to make him a new bow.

"What do you want with two?" said the father.

"This might break," he answered.

Pleased at the diligence of so small a boy, he made him a fine bow, and the next day he took it to his new friend in the tree. Wearied with that sport, they frolicked around the lodge and covered it with ashes. Suddenly the stranger said, "Your father is coming. I must go," and again the child sat still by the hearth.

"Why, my son," said the hunter, "you must have played hard to raise such a dust all alone."

"Yes," he answered, "I was very lonesome, and I ran round and round."

"Father," said the boy next day, "you must hunt till night and see what you can kill," and he was no sooner out of sight than the boys were once more at play together. As he neared home the hunter, from a piece of rising ground, caught a sound of laughter that seemed to come from two voices in his lodge, and just at this moment the stranger ran away to his retreat. The hunter found his son sitting quietly and unconcerned by the fire, but the articles of the lodge were strewn about in all directions.

"Why, my son," he said, "you must play very hard every day,

and what is it that you do, all alone, to throw the lodge into such confusion?"

"Father," he answered, "I play in this manner," and he began to chase and drag his blanket about so wildly that he sent his father laughing out of the lodge amid a great shower of ashes that nearly choked him.

The next night as he returned he again heard the sounds of play and laughter, and, as the wind was in just the right direction, he was sure that he heard two voices. The boy from the tree had just time to escape when the hunter again found his demure son by the fire, and the lodge in greater confusion than ever.

"My son," he said, "you must be very foolish when alone, to play so. But it certainly seemed that I heard two voices," and he then examined the ashes, and said: "Here is the print of a foot that is smaller than my son's."

The boy could no longer refuse to tell his father the truth. "I have found," he said, "a companion boy who lives in the hollow tree where you placed my mother's bones."

"Does my wife live again in this beautiful boy?" thought the hunter, and, fearful of disturbing the dead, he did not visit the hollow tree, but he persuaded his son to entice the boy to a dead tree by the edge of the wood, where they could shoot squirrels. At first the greenwood boy objected, saying that the father was near, but he was at last prevailed upon to go, and the hunter suddenly appeared and clasped the strange child in his arms.

"Kago, kago, don't, don't!" he cried. "You tear my clothes," which were fine and transparent.

By constant kindness and gentle words the boy was persuaded to remain with them, and the children were never parted, while in the newcomer the hunter seemed to feel the presence of his lost wife. In his gratitude to the Great Spirit he believed that this child would yet find a way to avenge him on the wicked Weendigoe who had destroyed the companion of his lodge. He grew at ease in his spirit, and passed all the time not actually needed for the chase in the company of the two children, who, though they were beautiful and well formed, neither of them grew in stature, but remained children still. Every day they grew more like each other, and they never wearied of playing in the innocent fashion of childhood. One day when the hunter was absent, the strange boy took one of the two shafts that had been left by the friendly Weendigoe, and when he returned with his food-supply, there lay the black giant who had slain his wife, dead beside the lodge door. He had been struck by the magic shaft, and the boy became the guardian genius of the lodge and no Weendigoe dared approach.

White Feather and the Six Giants. There was an old man living in the depth of a forest with his grandson whom he had taken in charge when he was an infant. The child's parents, brothers, and sisters had all been destroyed by six giants, and he had no other relatives. The band to whom he had belonged had put up their children on a wager against those of the giants' and had lost. There was a tradition in the tribe that one day it would produce a great man, who should wear a white feather, and who should astonish everyone by his feats of skill and bravery. As soon as the child could play about, his grandfather gave him bows and arrows, and one day, seeing a rabbit, he went home and described it to his grandfather, who told him what it was, and that its flesh was good to eat, and how he could kill it with his arrows. Thus encouraged, the boy became an expert hunter. One day he told his grandfather that he had seen lodge-poles standing, and ashes, and his grandfather said that that was impossible. But another day someone spoke to him and said:

"Come here, destined wearer of the white feather. Return home and take a short nap. You will dream of hearing a voice which will tell you to arise and smoke. You will see in your dream a pipe, a smoking sack, and a large white feather. When you wake you will find these articles. Put the feather on your head and you will become a great hunter, a great warrior, and a great man, able to do anything. As a proof that these things shall come to pass, when you smoke the smoke will turn to pigeons."

The voice informed him who he was, and that his grandfather was using him for his own ends. The voice-spirit then caused a vine to be laid at his side, and told him: "When you meet your enemy you will run a race with him. He will not see the vine because it is enchanted. While you are running you will throw it over his head and entangle him, so that you will win the race."

Long before this speech was ended the young man had turned to the quarter from which the voice came, and he was astonished to behold a man who was wood from the breast downward, and he seemed to be fixed in the earth. His countenance gradually faded and soon he was gone. All happened as the man had said, and the grandfather was greatly astonished to see a white feather on the boy's forehead, and pigeons flying out of the lodge. The young man departed next morning to find his enemies and avenge his race. When he arrived at the lodge of the six giants they began to make sport of him, and to say: "Here comes the little man with the white feather, who is to work such wonders."

Paying little attention to their jibes or their fine speeches, White Feather went fearlessly into their lodge and challenged them to a foot-match. Whoever won the stake was to use it to despatch the other. For five mornings he ran a race with a giant, and every time, by a dexterous use of the vine, he tripped him, and then cut off his head. The last of the giants resolved to succeed by craft. Before White Feather entered the sixth race the half-wooden man appeared to him and told him that a trick was to be played upon him.

"You," he said, "have never seen a woman, and the giant has arranged that you shall see the most beautiful one on earth. When she meets your eye, change yourself instantly into an elk, and go on feeding without looking at her again."

He went to the lodge, met the woman as foretold, and became an elk. She reproached him that he had cast aside the form of a man in order to avoid her.

"I have traveled a great distance," she said, "to see you and to marry you, for I have heard of your achievements and admire you very much."

This woman was really the sixth giant; but he had no suspicion, and her beauty and reproaches affected him so deeply that he wished himself a man again, and he at once resumed his natural shape. They sat down, and he began to make love to her. Soothed by her smiles and lulled by her voice, he fell asleep. Assuming her own form of the sixth giant, she took the feather from his brow, placed it upon her own head, and with a blow of her war-club changed him into a dog, in which degraded condition he was obliged to follow his captor into the lodge.

While these things were happening, two sisters, daughters of a chief, were fasting that they might have the good fortune to meet and love White Feather. Having heard of this the giant immediately set out with the dog to visit their lodges—for each had built one. When she saw the white feather, the eldest sister immediately invited the giant to her lodge and became his wife, while the other sister took the poor dog under her care. The giant went out boastfully to hunt, but he could catch nothing, while the dog ran out to the lake and drew out a stone which immediately became a beaver. The giant the next day repeated exactly what he had seen the dog do, and was delighted to see his stone turn to a beaver, which he tied to his belt. With great pride he bade his wife bring his hunting belt in, and behold! there was only a stone tied to it. The next day, finding that his method with the beaver had been discovered, the dog went to the wood and broke off the limb from a charred tree, which instantly became a bear. The giant, who always watched him, the next day carried home a bear, but when his wife went for it she found a burned stick. And so it continually happened. Everything prospered with the dog and failed with the giant. The giant's wife became so enraged that she decided to tell her father what a husband she had, who attempted to palm off stones and sticks as beavers and bears, and did not provide her with food, while the giant set out once more for a hunt. The dog signed to the younger sister to make him a little sweating-box with heated stones and water over them. Out of this came a fine young man without a voice, for that had somehow been sweated away. When the giant's wife reached her father's lodge she first entered upon the story of the absurd manner in which her sister was lavishing her love and care upon a dog, and she forgot her own grievance, which she had come to tell. The old chief suspected magic, and he immediately sent for his youngest daughter, with instructions to bring the dog; but in its place came a fine young man. The chief assembled a great company to smoke and take council on the situation. The pipe was handed first to the giant because of his white feather, and though he swelled and puffed, nothing but smoke came of it. It circled around until it came to the youth. He motioned that they should put the white feather upon his head, and when this was done he recovered speech and as he drew upon the pipe immense flocks of white and blue pigeons rushed from the smoke. It was then learned from the youth's story that the giant was an impostor, and the chief, who was a great magician, turned him into a dog.

The Winter Spirit and His Visitor. An old man was sitting alone in his lodge by the side of a frozen stream. It was the close of winter, and his fire was almost out. He appeared very old and very desolate. His locks were white with age, and he trembled in every joint. Day after day passed in solitude, and he heard nothing but the sounds of the tempest, sweeping before it the new-fallen snow. One day, as his fire was just dying, a handsome young man approached and entered his dwelling. His cheeks were red with the blood of youth; his eyes sparkled with life, and a smile played upon his lips. He walked with a light and quick step. His forehead was bound with a wreath of sweet grass, in place of the warrior's frontlet, and he carried a bunch of flowers in his hand.

"Ah! my son," said the old man, "I am happy to see you. Come in. Come, tell me of your adventures. What strange lands you have been to see. Let us pass the night together. I will tell you of my prowess and exploits, and what I can perform. You shall do the same, and we will amuse ourselves."

He drew from his sack a curiously wrought antique pipe, filled it, and handed it to his guest. "I blow my breath," the old man then continued, "and the streams stand still."

"I breathe," said the young man, "and flowers spring up over all the plains."

"I shake my locks," retorted the old man, "and snow covers the land. The birds fly to a distant land, and the animals hide themselves from the glance of my eye."

"I shake my ringlets," rejoined the young man, "and warm showers of soft rain fall upon the earth. The plants lift up their heads, and the eyes of children glisten. My voice calls back the birds, and my breath unlocks the streams."

The tongue of the old man became silent, and the robin and the bluebird began to sing in the top of the lodge.

Daylight fully revealed to the youth the character of his entertainer. When he gazed upon him streams began to flow from his eyes, and as the sun rose higher he became less and less in stature, and finally melted from sight. Nothing remained in the place of his lodge-fire but the little pink and white miskodeed, which Seegwun, the Spirit of Spring, placed in the wreath upon his brow, as his first trophy in the north.

Wunzh, the Father of Indian Corn. In time past—we cannot tell how many years ago—a poor Indian was living with his wife and children, in a beautiful part of the country. He was not only poor, but he had the misfortune to be inexpert in procuring food for his family, and his children were too young to help him. He was a man of kind and contented disposition, thankful to the Great Spirit for all that he received. He even stood at the door of his lodge to bless the birds that flew past in the summer evening. Had he been of a repining nature he might rather have complained because they were not furnishing his evening meal. His eldest son, who partook of the same sweet disposition, had arrived at the time of the fast.

Wunzh, for that was his name, had been an obedient son from infancy, and was greatly beloved by all. The father built for him the customary little lodge, and Wunzh strove to cleanse his heart of every evil thought, and he amused himself by walking in the woods and examining the early plants and flowers. He felt a strong desire to know how the berries grow, and the herbs, without aid from man, and why some were good for food and some poisonous. After he became too languid to walk about, he remained in the lodge, and he desired to dream of something that should prove of benefit to his family and all his fellow creatures. On the third day he suddenly fancied that a bright light came to the lodge door, and a handsome young man, with soft white face, came down from the sky and went toward him. He was richly dressed in green and yellow, and had a plume of waving feathers on his head.

"I am sent to you," said the visitor in a soft, musical voice, "by the Great Spirit who made all things in the sky and on the earth, to show you how you can do your kindred good. Arise, now, and wrestle with me."

Wunzh knew how weak he was, but the cheery voice of the stranger put courage in him, and he determined to die rather than fail. He was almost overpowered when the stranger said:

"My friend, it is enough. I will come again."

The next day he longed to see the celestial visitor and hear his voice, and to his great joy at sundown he was called to a second trial of strength by him. His strength of body was even less, but his courage was even greater, and the stranger again paused and said:

"To-morrow will be your last trial. Be strong, for only so can you gain what you desire;" and the light that shone as he departed was brighter than before. On the third day poor Wunzh was fainter than ever in body, but so strong in heart that he exerted every nerve until the stranger said:

"It is enough. You have conquered, and won from the Great Spirit your great desire. To-morrow I shall come for the last time. You must strip off my garments and throw me down, clean the earth of roots and weeds, make it soft, and bury me in the spot. Do not disturb my body in the earth, but come at times to visit the place and be careful never to let grass or weeds grow on my grave. Once a month cover me with fresh earth."

In the morning Wunzh's father came with some slight refreshment, saying: "My son, you have fasted long enough. If the Great Spirit will favor you, he will do it now. The Master of Life does not require the sacrifice of yours."

"My father, wait until the sun goes down," replied Wunzh.

As it was sinking he grasped his celestial challenger with supernatural strength, threw him down, and tearing off his fine garments and plume, and finding him already dead, he buried him just as he had been instructed.

Though Wunzh returned to his happy home, he never for a moment forgot the grave of his friend, and one day he saw the tops of green plumes coming through the earth, and as summer ended he asked his father to follow him to the spot where had stood his fasting-lodge. In the center of its circle rose a tall and graceful plant surmounted by nodding plumes. There was the deep green of the summer grass and the clear amber of the summer sky.

"It is my friend," shouted Wunzh, "the friend of all mankind. It is Moudawmin, our Indian corn! We need no longer rely on hunting, for as long as this gift is cherished the ground itself will give us food." So came that mighty blessing into the world through the dream of the brave boy, Wunzh.

The Bird-Lover. In a region of country where the forest and the prairie strove which should be the most beautiful, there lived a wicked manito in the disguise of an old Indian. Although the country furnished abundance of game it was the study of this wicked genius to destroy such as fell into his hands. He made use of all his arts to decoy men into his power in order to kill them. The country had been once thickly peopled, but this Mudjee Monedo had so thinned it that he now lived almost solitary. The secret